The Mediterranean

MANAGING EDITORS
Amy Bauman
Barbara J. Behm

CONTENT EDITORS
Amanda Barrickman
James I. Clark
Patricia Lantier
Charles P. Milne, Jr.
Katherine C. Noonan
Christine Snyder
Gary Turbak
William M. Vogt
Denise A. Wenger
Harold L. Willis
John Wolf

ASSISTANT EDITORS
Ann Angel
Michelle Dambeck
Barbara Murray
Renee Prink
Andrea J. Schneider

INDEXER
James I. Clark

ART/PRODUCTION
Suzanne Beck, Art Director
Andrew Rupniewski, Production Manager
Eileen Rickey, Typesetter

Library of Congress Number: 88-18337

  2   3   4   5   6   7   8   9   0   97   96   95   94   93   92

Library of Congress Cataloging-in-Publication Data

Fraissinet, Maurizio, 1957-
    [Mediterraneo. English]
    The Mediterranean / Maurizio Fraissinet, Bruno Massa,
Mario Milone.

    — (World nature encyclopedia)
    Translation of: Mediterraneo.
    Includes index.
    Summary: Describes the natural and ecological niches,
boundaries, and life of the wildlife habitats of the
Mediterranean.
    1. Ecology—Mediterranean Region—Juvenile literature.
2. Biotic and life of the wildlife habitats of the
Mediterranean.   1. Ecology—Mediterranean Region—
Juvenile literature.   2. Biotic communities—Mediterranean
Region—Juvenile literature.   [1. Ecology—Mediterranean
Region.   2. Biotic communities—Mediterranean Region.]
I. Massa, Bruno 1948-.   II. Milone, Mario, 1945.
III. Title.   IV. Series: Natura nel mondo. English.
QH150.F7313   1988   574.5′09182′2—dc19   88-18367
ISBN 0-8172-3325-3

WORLD NATURE ENCYCLOPEDIA

The Mediterranean

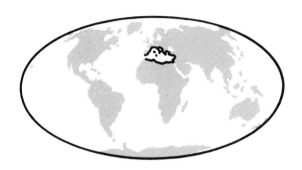

Maurizio Fraissinet
Bruno Massa
Mario Milone

RAINTREE
STECK-VAUGHN
L I B R A R Y

Austin, Texas

CONTENTS

6 INTRODUCTION

9 AN OVERVIEW
Mediterranean Characteristics, 9. The Straits, 10. Climate, 11. Volcanoes, 13. Islands and Ecology, 14. Nature Conservation, 18.

21 VEGETATION
Adaptations and Introductions, 21. Plant Associations, 22. Plants of the Maquis, 28. The Coastal Dunes, 31.

35 MEDITERRANEAN REPTILES
Lizards, 35. Snakes, 37. Tortoises and Turtles, 40.

43 BIRDS OF THE MAQUIS
Sylviids, 43. Other Birds, 44. Migration, 45. Wintering, 47. Bird Censuses, 48. Ornithological Observations, 53.

57 MAMMALS
Ungulates, 57. Rodents, 61. Barbary Ape, 63.

65 EAGLES AND VULTURES
Eagles, 65. Vultures: The Problem of Food, 66.

73 ROCKY COASTS
Mediterranean Herring Gull, 73. Audouin's Gull, 74. Shag, 75. Cory's Shearwater, 75. Peregrine Falcon, 77. Eleonora's Falcon, 78. Blue Rock Thrush, 79.

81 DELTAS AND COASTAL MARSHES
The Environments, 81. Seasons in the Marsh, 83.

89 LIFE IN THE SEA
The Abyssal Zones, 89. The Continental Shelf, 90.

97 SURVIVAL AND ECOLOGY
Effects of Habitat Destruction, 97. Mediterranean Monk Seal, 97. White-headed Duck, 99. Purple Gallinule, 100. Sea Turtle, 101.

105 GUIDE TO AREAS OF NATURAL INTEREST
Portugal, 106. Spain, 107. France, 109. Italy, 111. Yugoslavia, 113. Albania, 116. Greece, 116. Turkey, 118. Syria, 120. Israel, 120. Egypt, 121. Tunisia, 121. Algeria, 122. Morocco, 122.

123 GLOSSARY

126 INDEX

128 CREDITS

INTRODUCTION

On a late afternoon 400,000 years ago, a small group of men, women, and children built a camp on a hill that is now known as Terra Amata, Italy. They belonged to the species *Homo erectus*. This is the name scientists give to prehistoric people, those who lived before written history began. They had human bodies and brains but lived before *Homo sapiens*, or modern humans.

On Terre Amata, these people cut trees and shrubs. They hunted birds, elephants, Merk rhinoceroses, deer, wild boars, rabbits, and aurochs (big animals similar to oxen and buffalo). They fished for creatures with soft bodies inside shells like turtles, oysters, and limpets, and for a type of fish called stripe mullet. Today, the city of Nice stands where these people once lived, and there are no more traces of the ancient forest.

Neanderthals, the first modern humans or *Homo sapiens*, appeared about 300,000 years afterward. This race of people lived along the seacoast on reefs that no longer exist. They lived during the Ice Age, a time when ocean water turned to ice, causing the level of the sea to fall.

Cro-Magnons, a more advanced species of humans, followed. They hunted and gathered food to survive. When the last glaciers melted, from ten to forty thousand years

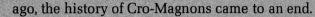

ago, the history of Cro-Magnons came to an end.

Next, between the years from 8000 B.C. to 3000 B.C., came a period of history called the Neolithic Age. During this time, people mined silver in Syria and copper in Cyprus. They grew flax, barley, and two kinds of wheat in what are now the countries of Syria and Palestine.

Since then, many civilizations have arisen on the lands that border the Mediterranean Sea. There were Aegeans and the people of the megaliths, which were huge stone monuments. There were Phoenicians and Etruscans who started navigation (traveling by water) and commerce (buying and selling things to and from people.

During the Middle Ages, from about A.D. 400 to A.D. 1500, the people around the Mediterranean were well organized. But the land was poor because of deforestation, a loss of trees resulting from decay and misuse by humans. People began to dream of moving to new lands where there would be plenty of wood and rich soil. They began to explore new places and develop colonies. Though the culture of the Mediterranean spread to new lands, the Mediterranean area itself lost importance, first as a political and economic center and then as a cultural one.

AN OVERVIEW

Geologists know little of the ancient Sea of Thetys that once covered the Mediterranean area. The present form of the Mediterranean basin developed sixty million years ago when the continent of Africa started to move north toward Europe.

Under the stress of enormous pressures, the earth's crust folded. The 971,400 square miles (2,516,000 square kilometers) of new sea, sprinkled with thousands of islands, then became surrounded by a series of mountain chains. In the north, the mountains formed in the shape of a boomerang, beginning with the Sierra Nevada in southern Spain, continuing through the Pyrenees and the French Massif Central, arching in the Swiss Alps, and ending with the Apennines of Italy, the Dinaric Alps, and the Balkan Mountains that scatter into the Greek Pindus Mountains.

The end of the Taurus Mountains, along the southern border of the Anatolian Plateau in Turkey, connects the Greek Pindus Mountains to the Aegean arc. The peaks of the Aegean arc rise above the water on the islands of Crete and Rhodes.

The Atlantic Ocean borders the Mediterranean on the west. Morocco and Algeria occupy its southwestern coast. To the east, the Mediterranean is bordered by the mountain chains of Lebanon that run along the Rift Valley from the Sea of Galilee through the Dead Sea to the Gulf of Aqaba and the Red Sea. The Sahara Desert, from the Qattara depression in northern Egypt to Tunisia, borders the east central Mediterranean. The altitude of the Qattara is 436 feet (133 meters).

Mediterranean Characteristics

Hydrography is the description and study of bodies of water. Understanding Mediterranean hydrography helps to better understand the Mediterranean region.

The mountain chains that surround both the Mediterranean basin and central Europe were covered with sheets of ice called "glaciers" for more than two millions years. These glaciers affected the formation of not only the mountains but also the nearby vegetation. The melting glaciers helped forests of trees with deciduous leaves (those that fall off each year) and evergreens to develop on the Mediterranean coasts.

They also fed and controlled the continental rivers which began in the Alps. These rivers are now known as the Rhine, the Danube, the Rhone, and the Po.

Preceding page: A little egret flies in the Mediterranean sky. This species is found here as well as other parts of the world. Like numerous others, it can find suitable habitats all year round in the basin. Egrets are often found in the delta and marsh areas.

Opposite page: The coast near Sapri is in the Gulf of Policastro. The Mediterranean coast offers both rocky and sandy shorelines. However, extremely high rocky cliffs and vast sandy shores have not formed mainly because of the comparatively gentle tides, the lack of violent storms, and the rivers that carry sediment and deposit it along the shore.

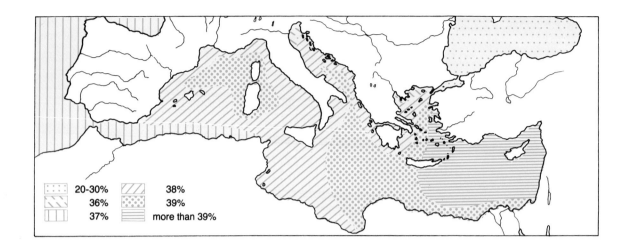

20-30%		38%	
36%		39%	
37%		more than 39%	

The map shows that the salt level of the surface waters of the Mediterranean gradually increases in an easterly direction. The water is saltiest in the warm Sea of Levant, where the surface water evaporates quickly and little river water enters. Compare this area with the low levels of salt in the Black Sea where fresh water from the Danube and Ukrainian rivers flows in.

The Straits

The waters and the weather of the Mediterranean are affected greatly by the straits that connect it to other bodies of water. The Strait of Gibraltar links the Mediterranean with the Atlantic Ocean. The Dardanelles and the Bosporus are straits that connect it with the Black Sea. The Suez Canal connects it with the Red Sea.

The Dardanelles separates the Aegean Sea, an arm of the Mediterranean between Asia Minor and Greece, from the smaller Sea of Marmara, which is inland from the Mediterranean. The Black Sea flows into the Sea of Marmara through the Bosporus Straits.

Many birds use the Dardanelles and the Bosporus, as well as Gibraltar, as passages during their spring and fall migrations, when they move from one geographic area and climate to another. As a result, these straits are of great interest to ornithologists, scientists who study birds.

The Suez Canal, built in 1869, has been the center of much controversy. The canal allowed the Mediterranean and Red seas to mix. As a result, fifteen species (groups of related individuals capable of producing offspring) of Red Sea fish appeared in the eastern Mediterranean. This meant there was less food to go around, and it became harder for the fish that were there before to find enough to eat. No Mediterranean species has disappeared, but none has thrived in the Red Sea, either.

The last important influence on the evolution of the climate and the plant and animal communities of the Mediterranean is the Strait of Gibraltar. It formed from a powerful upward movement of the earth's surface and separated the

The Rock of Gibraltar is actually the point of a rock that juts out from an underwater barrier separating the waters of the Mediterranean from those of the Atlantic Ocean. Inhabitants of Gibraltar aptly call it "the island" for the weather around the rock is often different from the rest of the peninsula. A dark cloud called the "Levanter" often hovers over Gibraltar, even when the sky is perfectly clear in the region nearby. This cloud causes heavy rains that are about double that of the surrounding coastal regions of Andalusia. Because of this unique climate, at least six hundred species of plants and flowers have developed on the Rock, many of them only being found there. Gibraltar is also famous for the Barbary ape, the only monkey now inhabiting the European continent.

Mediterranean waters from those of the Atlantic. The Mediterranean became a large lake, like none other on the globe.

The water of the strait itself is no more than 1,310 feet (400 m) deep. About 150 miles (240 km) west of the strait, it drops off quickly to a depth of 10,660 feet (3,250 m). In contrast, as the strait flows east into the Mediterranean, it is only about 8,200 feet (2,500 m) deep at the Balearic Islands.

Climate

The Strait of Gibraltar moderates the temperature of the Mediterranean so that it is neither very hot nor very cold. The surface temperature of the Mediterranean is about 50° to 60° Fahrenheit (10° to 15° Celsius) in winter. In the

Below is a majestic example of the famous and beautiful olive tree. Native to the eastern Mediterranean, the olive tree has been continually transplanted since ancient times until it is now found everywhere around the Mediterranean. *(See the map, opposite page.)* In the time of the ancient Hebrews, the olive branch was a symbol of peace. Today, the olive tree is the plant that is the trademark of the Mediterranean. At maturity, olive trees have gray, hollow trunks. They grow as high as 32 feet (10 m). The small, spear-shaped leaves are olive green on top and silver underneath. The fruit is known everywhere and entire economies have been based on its cultivation.

summer, it climbs as high as 82°F (28°C) at the Sea of Levant in the far eastern end. Deep water reaches temperatures of 55°F (13°C). The average air temperature varies from around 40° to 50°F (5° to 10°C) in autumn and winter to 70° to 77°F (21° to 25°C) during the summer.

Because the sea covers a very large area, Mediterranean weather is mild like that of the ocean, with a lot of rain. Summers are warm and humid on the northern side and dry and desertlike in the south. The average rainfall is around 16 to 28 inches (400 to 700 millimeters). A minimum of 8 inches (200 mm) of rain falls in the Suez Canal. A maximum of around 55 inches (1,400 mm) falls in the cities of Genoa (northwest Italy) and Marseilles (southeast France). It almost never snows in those parts of the Mediterranean region that are located at less than 1,600 feet (500 m). The warm water of

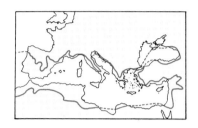

the Mediterranean lying so near the cold Atlantic water causes cyclones to develop in the winter in some areas.

In summer, the winds are mostly southern. Those from the Canary Islands off the coast of Africa bring warm and humid air. Hot, dry winds blowing from the Sahara cause droughts (long periods of dryness). Mountain ranges that circle the basin help to keep the temperature in the area pleasant and mild.

Evaporation, the process whereby water changes to vapor or moisture in the air continues into autumn, drying up rivers and streams. This climate cannot support fast-growing plants with shallow roots such as underbrush and ground cover, which keep soil from washing away or eroding. This erosion is made worse by alternating seasons of extreme drought and heavy rain.

The typical soil of the Mediterranean has a red color common to areas rich in hematite, an iron ore. This type of soil, combined with the climate, helps many types of vegetation grow, from the trees of the forests to the lowly maquis, the scrubby vegetation of the coast.

Two species of birds thrive in the same climate and conditions as these common trees and shrubs. The black-eared wheatear, a chat or songbird, and the white throat, an Old World warbler, can be found throughout most of the Mediterranean except for some areas in North Africa and the Near East. There is a close relationship between the environment and the plant and animal species in the Mediterranean.

Volcanoes

The land masses of Europe, Asia, and Africa slowly move because of enormous heat beneath the earth's surface. When this heat finds its way to thinner places in the earth's crust, earthquakes and volcanoes result. In the Mediterranean basin today, these eruptions happen mostly in the south-central area where there are two volcanic island circles. One is the Aeolian, north of Sicily, and the other is the Aegean, north of Crete.

Three volcanoes of the Aeolian Circle were active in ancient times. Stromboli is still one of the most active volcanoes in the world. Vulcano, which was the mythical home of Aeolus, the king of winds, has many fumaroles, openings from which smoke and gases rise. Lipari, made up of white pumice and black obsidian rock, has been dormant since the eighth century.

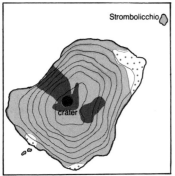

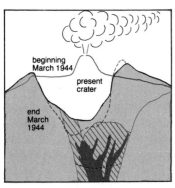

Above: This map marks areas where volcanoes were active in historical times. *Center:* The volcanic island of Stromboli with the Strombolicchio reef nearby. This volcano, which has been continuously active for centuries, has underwater origins and ascends in two peaks, the highest of which is 3,038 feet (926 m). The volcano throws out lava, cinders, and lapilli (small stones) on the sea along the slope (indicated in red on the diagram) called "Sciara del Fuoco" (Rocks of Fire). *Below:* A cross-section of Mt. Vesuvius is shown.

Opposite page: Explosive activity in the crater northeast of Etna is photographed as it spews out materials and emits sulfurous vapors.

In the Aegean Circle, the most famous volcano is Santorini. The Greek historian Herodotus wrote of it as the mysterious Atlantis. It was also known as Kalliste, "the most beautiful." Santorini erupted violently in 1370 B.C. and formed a caldera, a broad crater that is created when a volcano's cone collapses. This happened again in 1883 when Krakatoa erupted in Indonesia, throwing out more than 5 cubic miles (20 cu km) of material.

Volcanoes were named for Vulcan, the Roman god of fire. Mt. Etna was said to be his forge (workplace). This volcano is the largest in Europe at 10,725 feet (3,269 m). It is famous not only because it is still active but also because it has a unique, complex structure. About three hundred cones can be found on its surface, and it looks like a huge dragon with a hundred mouths. The shape of Pantelleria is different from that of Mt. Etna. Like most other volcanoes, Pantelleria has a simple cone. It rises to 2,742 feet (836 m) above the sea. Pantelleria's last eruption was in 1904. But it is still known to be active because of the hot springs, which sometimes contain sulfur, found running into streams along the coast.

The area around Naples, a city in Italy, is unique because it contains two different examples of volcanoes.

There are active craters in the Phlegraean Fields west of Naples. It is here that prehistoric people made up stories, or myths, about a series of explosions. They were said to be huge fights between Cyclopses (giants with one huge eye in the middle of its forehead) and the Titans.

From Naples west to the ruins of Cumae, and from the island Ischia to the volcano Pozzuoli, the Phlegraen Fields now show nineteen craters in an area of about 25 sq. miles (65 sq. km). Sometimes the rings of these craters are broken by other eruptions.

Today, the activity of the volcanoes can be seen as Pozzuoli and Solfarata slowly give off gases and fumes. The activity also can be seen under the water, near the slopes of Pozzuoli, Baia, and Bacoli.

Islands and Ecology

Until the 1960s, biologists tried to learn about the movement of species and their habitats by studying where land masses were located long ago. For example, the presence of many African species on the island of Sicily was explained by a bridge of land that may have once existed between Sicily and Africa. In the same way, many species

common to land east of the Adriatic Sea appeared west of the sea in Puglia, the "heel" of Italy. This was explained by a bridge between the Gargano peninsula and the Dalmatian coast of Yugoslavia.

However, this doesn't always explain the presence of certain species in isolated habitats or islands. Other factors must also be considered. For example, a species may have spread actively by itself, or passively, transported by others.

The development of these species depends mostly on ecological factors, or how they react to their resources and surroundings. In 1963, two American ecologists proposed the theory of dynamic equilibrium of the species based on some of these factors.

These scientists believed that the mixture of species on an island at any moment is influenced by two factors that change with time. One is immigration, the moving in of new species. The number of species that live on the continent closest to the island, and their movements, affect island ecology. Also, species are not likely to immigrate to islands far from the mainland, since it is hard to cross a large span of sea.

The other is extinction. A species may become extinct, or disappear, because the number of individuals in the

species is too small to survive. Other reasons for extinction are competition between species, and changes in the land, water, or air of the island.

According to the theory of dynamic equilibrium, there is a constant balance between the number of species immigrating and the number becoming extinct. French ecologist Jacques Blondel has reported examples of this theory on Mediterranean islands. This scientist and his colleagues studied the bird life on the island of Corsica.

On Corsica, the total number of species is lower than that on an equal area of nearby mainland. This is because of the strait that lies between Corsica and the mainland. The species living on the island have a greater ecological niche than those on the continent because the variety of species is smaller. An ecological niche is the role or function of a species within its community and environment.

Also, given the same habitat, the species reach higher population densities. This means that there is a larger number of individuals within an area of a given size on the island than in an area of the same size on the mainland.

Scientists have discovered that the species living on Corsica are those from the continent that have the greatest

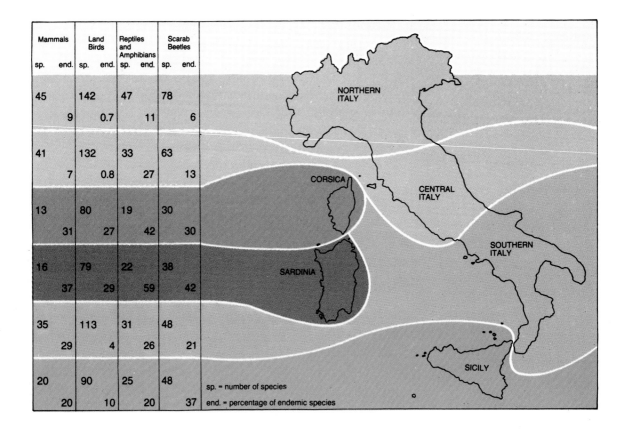

Mammals		Land Birds		Reptiles and Amphibians		Scarab Beetles	
sp.	end.	sp.	end.	sp.	end.	sp.	end.
45	9	142	0.7	47	11	78	6
41	7	132	0.8	33	27	63	13
13	31	80	27	19	42	30	30
16	37	79	29	22	59	38	42
35	29	113	4	31	26	48	21
20	20	90	10	25	20	48	37

sp. = number of species

end. = percentage of endemic species

The table traces the numbers of species on the Italian peninsula from the mainland down to areas that are more or less surrounded by the sea. Fewer varieties of animals turn up on the land that is more sea-bound. Because of its narrow, long shape, this land mass was an ideal place to test the theory of equilibrium. Though fewer types of animals can be found, the number of endemic species is greater. These species are found in isolated areas that are similar to islands. The table shows the number of species and the number of endemic species on three large Mediterranean islands.

ecological valence, or ability to adapt to new and different habitats. This is also true for the islands of Sardinia and Sicily, as well as others in the Mediterranean.

Nature Conservation

Nature conservation is a way of protecting endangered species by providing them with a natural habitat. For those studying the problems of nature conservation, the theory of equilibrium is a useful tool.

When ecologists establish a nature conservation area, they are setting up a system similar to an island. In both places, the species live there because the environment is just right for them. But, just as the theory suggests, the number of species that can live together in a nature reserve depends on the size of the area and whether or not it is isolated. Large reserves and reserves close to one another can protect a greater number of species. Small, isolated reserves are islands in the sense that they support a species that could not survive outside of that reserve.

An endemic species is an animal or plant whose habi-

The painted frog is an amphibian without a tail that is mainly found in North Africa. In smaller numbers, these frogs inhabit the European part of the Mediterranean basin, especially islands such as Sardinia and Sicily. At present, they have reached the Hyeres Islands near the French coast as they slowly travel toward Europe.

tat is limited to a specific geographic region. The habitats of true island species are isolated or set apart from others, so scientists call these species endemic island species. They are of great interest because, by being isolated, they have developed obvious traits that make them different from other species.

On the other hand, plants and animals that live in large territories, such as continents, have characteristics that are the result of very gradual changes in a large population. To recognize these differences, scientists must carefully compare many groups of the species in the area.

Only a few members survive in some endemic populations. In these cases, the group is in danger of dying out because of genetic drift. Genetic drift refers to changes in how often genes are likely to be passed on. Genes determine the characteristics that are passed on from one generation to the next. And whether certain genes are passed on may just be a matter of chance. The members of small groups of species are more likely to be hurt by random changes in the frequency of harmful genes than members of large groups.

As a small group moves toward extinction, a new species often takes its place. This happens a lot among the species found on islands.

VEGETATION

Among the geographic regions of the Old World (the Eastern Hemisphere, including Europe, Asia, and Africa), the Mediterranean basin has by far the biggest variety of plants. In Greece, for example, more than six thousand species of flowering plants have been found. This is almost four times the number found in Great Britain. The small land areas of the Mediterranean can accommodate incredible numbers of plant species.

For instance, there are one thousand different kinds of plants on Mount Parnassus, near Athens, and in the area surrounding Jerusalem. Many species found in certain areas of the Mediterranean are not found anywhere else. One-quarter of the flowering plant species of the Balkan Peninsula (composed of Yugoslavia, Bulgaria, Albania, and Greece) are found nowhere else in the world. On the island of Crete, there are 131 plant species that are found only on that island. Sixty-nine are found on the small island of Cyprus. Such variety comes not only from the favorable climate but also from the many small peninsulas and islands.

Adaptations and Introductions

The most common Mediterranean plants are evergreens with small, tough leaves. These leatherlike, wax-coated leaves are the plants' way of adapting to the extreme heat and summer drought. The leaves lose little water so that each plant is able to store its own water supply. Many plants also store water in their stems and roots.

Generally, the Mediterranean-style vegetation doesn't exist above about 2,300 feet (700 m). Above that, woods of oak, hornbeam, and Spanish chestnut trees, normally found in mountain foothills, take over.

While the glaciers of the Ice Age caused big changes in the species of plants found in most of Europe, they had very little effect on those in the Mediterranean basin. In fact, the ice rarely descended lower than 8,900 feet (2,700 m) in the Mediterranean region. As a result, several ancient plants still exist there today: carob trees, myrtles, oleanders, plane trees, mastic shrubs, and Judas trees. It is certain that there were other plant species like these that later disappeared during the ice ages. Today, in addition to these plants, there are many other new species.

Finally, other plants were brought by people to the Mediterranean during different periods of history. The olive tree, the common fig tree, and the pomegranate were probably brought by the Greeks or the Phoenicians from the Far East.

Opposite page: The fruit of the strawberry tree is one of the most colorful aspects of the Mediterranean maquis. During much of the year, little snow white flowers appear on the tree as well.

Below: The eastern growing area of the cork oak is shown in red and the western growing area of the Valonia oak is shown in blue. This growing pattern divides the Mediterranean into separate halves.

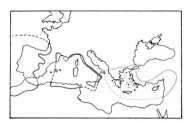

La Giara di Gesturi is a plateau in central Sardinia where the Mediterranean environment has remained unchanged because of its isolated location. These highlands are covered with many cork oak trees and fern and cistus grow beneath them. Water is plentiful because of the huge rain pools that form on this plateau. Because the basalt soil does not absorb the water, these pools exist throughout most of the year except in summer when the sun evaporates them. This is where the last herds of European wild horses still graze. They are known as ponies because of their small size.

The lime tree came with the Arabs, who had received it from China. The century plant and prickly pear, on the other hand, were brought from the New World (the Western Hemisphere, including North and South America) in the sixteenth century.

In the last few centuries, the introduction of new plants has continued, both for economic and decorative purposes. For these reasons came the eucalyptus and some acacias from Australia, palms from the Canary Islands, bougainvillea from Brazil, and the Hottentot fig from South Africa.

Plant Associations

Plants growing in the same area interact and affect each other, forming characteristic plant associations. This process, called "plant succession," is also influenced by animals. Over time, it allows new species to take root in soil

Plant species from other continents have flourished in the Mediterranean environment. Eucalyptus from Australia, agave and Indian fig from Central America, and Hottentot fig from South Africa are now part of the landscape.

that gradually has been changed by the preceding species. Eventually, a stable, final equilibrium is reached that conforms with the local climate, geography, geology, and other conditions. This final stage is called "climax."

The climax that develops naturally in a Mediterranean region is either a forest of evergreen oaks or pines. There are very few forests of this kind today, but some can be found in hard-to-reach areas where people haven't yet intruded.

The most typical climax forest is made up of holm or evergreen oak trees. These trees are 40 to 50 feet (12 to 15 m) high. Underneath lies a layer of strawberry tree, viburnum, creeping honeysuckle, greenbriar, and blackbryony. The thick vegetation blocks sunlight from the ground. This means very few herbaceous (green-leafed) plants can survive.

In the far eastern Mediterranean, the holm oak is

Raw cork just harvested is stacked at the edge of the plantation to dry naturally. The bark of the cork oak is first removed when the trunk grows to a circumference of 11 to 15 inches (30 to 40 cm). At that time, a raw product called "male cork" or "rough cork" is obtained. From nine to twelve years later, when the bark is about 1 inch (3 cm) thick, the cork is removed again. This "fine cork" or "female cork" is valued more because it is more compact and has an even texture.

replaced by the kermes oak, a cone-bearing spiny oak tree.

In the southern part of the Iberian Peninsula are vast woods of cork oak. These cork oak trees have formed a strange association with dwarf fan palms, plants with palm leaves on prickly stalks.

In areas that are dry and sunny, other climax associations develop. The Oleo-Ceratonium is widely scattered and consists of sparse olive and carob trees associated with myrtle, tree heath, strawberry tree, broom, and cistus. Sometimes, the carob tree is associated with the dwarf fan palm. In the lime-rich and sandy soils of the dry regions, Aleppo pine forests can develop. The cluster pine (widespread from Spain to Italy) and the Italian stone pine form forests in the areas overlooking the coastline and among the coastal sand dunes. In the Balkan Peninsula and on the islands of the Aegean Sea and Dalmatia (southern coast of Yugoslavia) are Italian cypress and sweet bay laurel forests.

Shown in the drawings are examples of four types of Mediterranean vegetation. Evergreen forests are still found in a few areas but are becoming more and more scarce. They characterized by oaks such as holm oak, spiny kermes oak, cork oak, and valonia oak or by pines like Aleppo, cluster pine, and stone pine. Maquis of small trees and shrubs often grow nearby. The maquis is composed of a thick undergrowth of shrubs like strawberry tree and juniper. Some trees with tall trunks like oak or pine appear above the maquis. As the trees and taller shrubs disappear, the guarigue takes over with scattered bushes like cistus and dwarf fan palm which grow on arid and stony soils. The steppe appears where even the lowest shrubs cannot grow in the worn-out soil. Only grasses grow there.

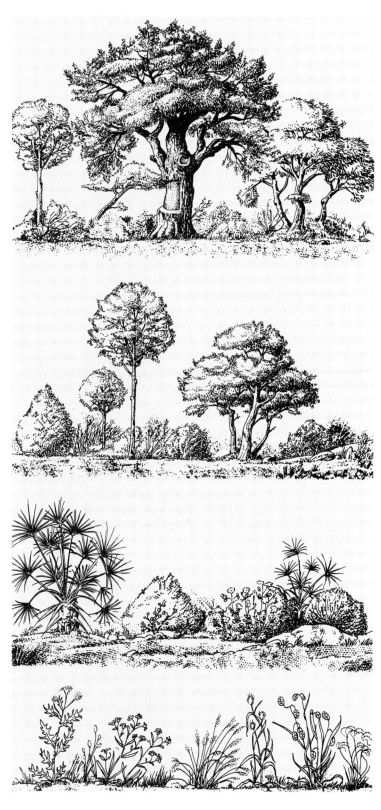

Flowering maquis flourish at Capo
Matalfano, at the far southern points of
the Sardinian coast. Maquis may be of
two types: the primary, which are the
original, primitive type, or the secondary,
which have changed as a result of
evolution. In general, it has been said
that the maquis is the "woody plant
community most representative of the
Mediterranean."

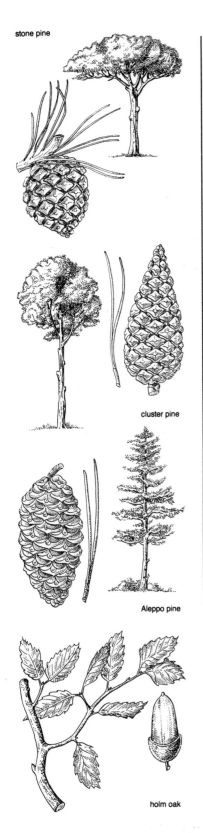

stone pine

cluster pine

Aleppo pine

holm oak

A forest thinned out by people or nature slowly becomes a maquis. A maquis consists of shrubs about 7 feet (2 m) tall. Tall maquis contain strawberry trees, junipers, Aleppo pine, tree heath, and wild olive. Low maquis have mastic shrub, myrtle, rosemary, and butcher's broom. Rock-rose plants, which have white or red-violet flowers, are common in maquis. A mixed maquis has mastic shrub, carob tree, and myrtle.

Today the maquis is the most frequent plant association in the Mediterranean. It is hard to identify which plants of the maquis formed the original forest, and which plants sprang up at the climax stage. These plant communities do not develop any farther. The maquis is thick and often impossible to penetrate.

The decay of the maquis from damage by people or fire gives birth to the association known as "garigue." Its unique characteristic as a plant association is its bushy plants. They are spread either on the hillsides or among dry, sunny rocks. In Greece, the garigue is known as "phrygana," and contains as many as two hundred species of plants. In Spain, it is called "tomillares" and is mostly made up of thyme, sage, and lavender.

The brightly colored blossoms of the garigue usually bloom in April, right before the beginning of the long, hot summer drought. These two factors—heat and drought—force plants to protect themselves. Some plants have small, thick leaves. There are also many resinous, or milky, plants. These plants have sap flowing in veins which store the scarce water by taking it from the soil and circulating it through their stems. The most common plants in the garigue, besides thyme, rosemary, sage, and lavender, are some spurge and various crocuses, rockroses, and irises.

Overgrazing by animals in pastures and sweeping fires destroy even shrubby plants and bare the soil, exposing it to erosion. When erosion weakens the soil, the only plants that can exist are herbaceous. They make up the classic Mediterranean steppe, also found in other parts of the world. The most common plants in a steppe are thistle, giant fennel, mullein, clover, anemone, sea poppy, and asphodel.

Plants of the Maquis

The crown of the maquis and the Mediterranean forest is the holm oak. It can reach 40 to 50 feet (12 to 15 m) in height. Its higher leaves are dark green, while its bottom leaves are lighter. On higher branches, the leaves are narrow

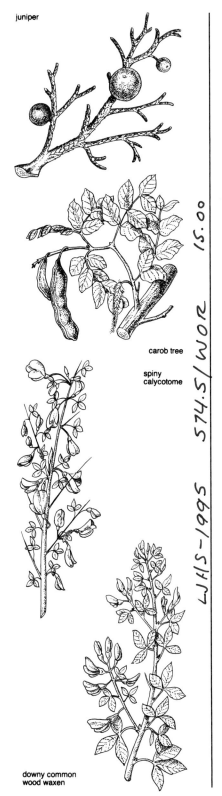

juniper

carob tree

spiny calycotome

downy common wood waxen

and tough, with smooth edges. On the lower branches, the leaves are serrated, or notched like a saw. They are similar to those of holly. Thus, the holm oak is also called the holly oak. The holm oak can live over three hundred years.

The carob tree is also typically Mediterranean. It is linked to the history of the people who lived around this sea, especially those in the far eastern areas. In ancient oriental history, the carob tree was an important source of food for both people and their animals. The carob is nutritious, containing about 40 to 50 percent sugar and 7 percent protein. The plant is particularly hearty. Thriving in even the driest and sunniest places, it grows 30 to 50 feet (10 to 15 m) tall. Its leaves are green and glossy, and each leaf is made up of several tiny leaves, or leaflets. It bears green fruit that browns when it ripens, like most pod-bearing plants.

The strawberry tree is a common shrub or small tree of the maquis. It seldom grows taller than about 33 feet (10 m). Its trunk has many branches which sprout small white flowers and fruit in autumn. The round, bumpy berries become red and sweet when they ripen. They are an important food source for migratory birds.

Myrtle bushes appear in groups. The leaves are small and pointed with small, dark blue berries. White, sweet-smelling flowers bloom from the end of May to July. The myrtle plant was associated with Venus, the Roman goddess of beauty. It was used to braid wreaths to crown sports winners, judges, and poets. From the leaves of the myrtle comes an oil used called "angel water." It is used in some perfumes.

Another maquis plant with a special place in history is the sweet bay laurel. The laurel tree can grow over 30 feet (10 m) tall. It has dark green, strong-smelling leaves. In ancient history, the laurel was considered sacred to the Greek god Apollo, and laurel wreaths were used to crown sages, or wise people. This tree gave us the terms, *laureate* or distinguished expert, and, *becca laureate* or bachelor's degree, in college.

The mastic tree is an evergreen plant 3 to 7 feet (1 to 2 m) tall, with fragrant leaves. The mastic has small flowers grouped in dense spikes like the quills of a porcupine. These quickly produce bunches of red, pea-sized fruit, which later turn black. The mastic thrives on dry slopes exposed to the sun, particularly if they slope toward the sea, and it is unaffected by wind. If the trunk is cut open, a substance called resin can gather. In the past, this resin was

29

With their large, perfumed flowers, cistuses add enchantment to the springtime scene near the maquis and the guarigue. The marine cistus, shown here, is white, and the sage-leaved cistus is pink. Livestock avoid this shrubby species, so it freely spreads over wide areas.

used to make varnishes. It also has been used as chewing gum since the ancient Greek times.

Tree heath, a short plant covering the ground around trees, is a common ingredient of the strawberry tree maquis. It can overtake an area when the soil becomes too acid and loses salts. Tree heath usually grows 3 to 13 feet (1 to 4 m) tall, but can sometimes reach 30 to 50 feet (10 to 15 m). It has thin, needlelike leaves. In the spring, it produces white or pale rose-colored flowers in the shape of little bells. The hard roots of this plant are so thick they are called briars. Some tobacco pipes are made from them.

The various species of cistus are bushy plants, with woody stalks and small leaves. Their large, colored flowers attract many insects. They are a common plant of the Mediterranean garigue.

A distinctly southern shrub that grows along the waterways or on the banks of dry streams is the oleander. It has narrow, pointed, thick leaves and large, pink, fragrant flowers. It is seen in the western Mediterranean, southern Spain, and Morocco.

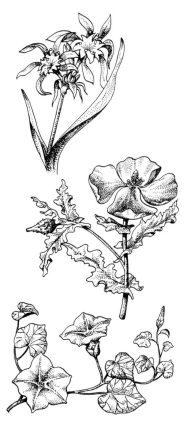

The dwarf fan palm is characteristic of the western Mediterranean coastal maquis. It is also found in the garigue and the steppe. It is usually only a foot or two tall, but in a few cases (mainly in Morocco), it grows up to 10 to 13 feet (3 to 4 m) tall. It is the only one of its species to originate in Europe. Its fronds, or leafy, fernlike branches, look like superhuman hands with ten to twenty fingers spread out. These "fingers," or leaves, are held together by a prickly, woody stem. Its fruit cannot be eaten. The fronds are used for weaving and for making brooms.

The shrubs called "spurge" belong to the Euphorbiaceae family, which has relatives in all the warm areas of the world. These bushy plants are common in the garigue. Inside the stalks of spurge is a milky juice called latex.

In the Mediterranean, a common and widespread species of spurge is *Euphorbia dendroides*. This plant is round with tiny, green-gray leaves. In the spring, clusters of yellow blossoms that look like flowers, but actually are not, surround the leaves like a shell and protect them.

The Coastal Dunes

In the Mediterranean countries until the 1950s, there were still many miles of dunes along the shores. In the few

31

Below: A view is provided of the pond and dunes in Coto Doñana, a Spanish national park at the mouth of the Guadalquivir River. These dunes are among the highest and most beautiful in Europe.

Opposite page: Two beetles of the coastlines are shown. Above is the predator *carabid Cicindela circumdata* and below is the *Pimelia rugulosa* that feeds on vegetation waste and dwells in dark places. Beetles, or the coleoptera group, are found everywhere. Not only are they the largest order of insects, but they are the largest order of all living things. After years of research, experts have accounted for more than 300,000 known species, but all agree that this number is just an estimate, and probably on the low side.

decades since then, the dunes have been cultivated and covered with natural dikes and windbreakers, such as tamarisk trees and various species of pine. Today, therefore, there are few true coastal dunes.

The vegetation there is unique to the environment. The beach, being so close to the sea, is fertile ground for plants like wheatgrass. This is a hearty grass with strong, large tufts and creeping rhizomes, or shallow roots. It forms a base on which other vegetation, such as sea holly, sea parsley, moonwort, searocket, and inula can grow. The sea laps up on the beach and near the dunes, which may be found either alone or in groups. In the recently formed dunes are new plant associations of sand-loving grasses such as European beach grass, medick, crosswort, and chamomile.

These plants have found ways to adapt to their sandy

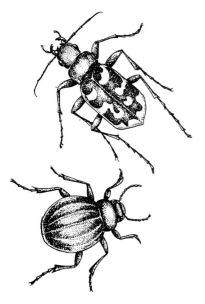

home. For example, the more succulent species, those best able to retain water, have water reserves. Water is held by the thin, rounded leaves of some Gramineae, the thick covering of soft hairs on some plants, and the formations of bushes resembling long, thick scouring pads.

There are also native species, which have adapted to the sandy environment. Close to the sea are found tiny crustaceans (sea animals with crusty shells), such as sand-hopper or beach fleas. Also found is *Eurynebria complanata*, a horned beetle that blends into the sand because it is almost the same color.

Other insects found there include large Scarabaeidae, beetles with powerful jaws, and tiger beetles, expert flyers that feed mostly on the larvae (eggs) of other insects and crustaceans.

MEDITERRANEAN REPTILES

In the countries bordering the Mediterranean Sea, there are almost two hundred species of amphibians and reptiles. They make their homes in all the different habitats of the region, proving that reptiles and amphibians can adapt to different living conditions.

The world of the Mediterranean reptiles could be defined as a world of rustling noises. The longer the body of the reptile, the more rustling noise it makes, whether it's a lizard or a snake.

Lizards

Lizards are mostly insectivores (insect-eaters), and as a result, there are a lot of them. There are several families of lizards, some of which are common.

A family is a classification of plants or animals made up of related genuses (groups of species). True lizards belong to the family Lacertidae. More than thirty different species are found along the Mediterranean.

The most common lizard of this family is the emerald lizard. Up to 20 inches (50 cm) long, it is bright green. The male's head turns blue during the reproductive period. Another common lizard, the jewelled lizard, is even longer. It may reach 30 inches (75 cm). It has large, round, sky-blue spots on a green-and-brown background.

Another family of lizards, Scincidae, are called "skinks." They have smaller legs than the Lacertidae lizards. The *Chalcides ocellatus,* one member of the Scincidae family, is found all over much of Asia, southern Europe, and Africa. In the Mediterranean, this lizard is found in Greece, Asia Minor, North Africa, and on the islands of Sardinia and Sicily.

Short, squat, and covered with very smooth scales, the Chalcides ocellatus generally grows no longer than 12 inches (30 cm). It moves almost like a snake, with its very short legs and a body shaped like a long cylinder. It prefers dry, sandy locations with very little vegetation where there are ravines and holes in which it can hide. It feeds on snails, and large piles of leftover shells can be found inside its den. It also catches insects and completes its diet with small, juicy leaves. It is ovoviviparous, producing eggs that hatch inside the mother's body. The female gives birth to up to three young.

The Anguidae are glass lizards that have many species completely lacking legs, yet are still quite different from snakes. One difference is that their eyes have moving eye-

Opposite page: Stony locations, maquis, and meadows are the favorite surroundings of the Aesculapian snake. This tree-climbing reptile can move quickly but is not easily provoked. Growing as large as 6 feet (2 m), it is active during the day and is found on plains, hills, and mountains up to 5,905 feet (1,800 m).

Some European reptiles are not snakes. *Above, from left to right: Agama stellio* is lively but harmless despite its appearance; the large and aggressive ocellated green lizard; the chameleon, acrobat of the shrubs. *Below:* the shy European tortoise, *Chalcides ocellatus,* and finally the small *Chalcides chalcides* with its almost non-existent legs.

lids like humans. The *Pseudopus apodus* of Dalmatia can grow as long as 3 feet (1 m). The common gecko is the best known representative of the Gekkonidae family. Geckos are widespread, not being limited to the Mediterranean. The gecko is known for its ability to climb on surfaces as smooth as glass. This is because it has countless fine bristles on the bottom of its toes which are able to hook onto even the tiniest rough surfaces. Similar to a tiny prehistoric monster, the gecko comes out most often on summer nights, when it lives almost in complete harmony, or symbiosis, with humans. The gecko takes advantage of every light that people leave on to hunt its favorite prey: moths, mosquitoes, and other insects. Once it spots the prey, the gecko slowly stalks along the wall until it is within 2 inches (5 cm) of its prey. Suddenly the gecko springs ahead, trapping the insect in its huge jaws.

Not to be confused with the gecko is the hardun, found on Corfu (an Ionian Island), on the Sporades of the Aegean Seas and around Thessalonica in Greece and Alexandria in Egypt. It is the only European representative of the family Agamidae, which is widespread in Asia and Africa. It looks a bit like a dragon and lives by visiting sunny low walls and hunting insects.

The most specialized of the Mediterranean lizards is undoubtedly the African chameleon. It has some unusual

characteristics, including its changeable color. This is due to special movements of a pigment called "melanin" in its skin. The chameleon can blend into the background and be disguised wherever it sits, especially among vegetation and on sandy, pebbly ground.

The chameleon also has specialized feet. Its toes are fused in two small pincers, useful for grabbing small branches.

Snakes

Snakes are different from lizards in that their spinal cords are more flexible, and they do not have legs. Some lizards, such as the Anguidae (glass lizards), also lack legs. Snakes also have fixed and transparent eyelids and only one lung. They feed mostly on vertebrates (animals with backbones) from mammals to fish. The prey is, in fact, bigger than the snake itself.

The most common loud rustling in the Mediterranean countries is often made by the rat snake, or by some other species of the genus *Elaphe* (Aesculapian snake, leopard snake, or ladder snake) or *Natrix* (water snakes). Less often the noises come from the adder. This snake is not as common as the nonpoisonous species.

The rat snake can be a variety of colors, from yellow-green to black. It can reach 60 inches (150 cm) in length. It is found in small numbers in all kinds of environments. Among its prey are the emerald lizard and other species of lizards.

The leopard snake is an elegant one, with a series of red spots ringed in black on a gray background. It grows to a length of 3 feet (1 m) and feeds mostly on small mammals. While it is young, it also preys on many lizards. The leopard snake is seldom seen and is even disappearing in some parts of the Balkan Peninsula and southern Italy. This is because the river maquis environment in which it lives is deteriorating. The genus *Elaphe* is made up of other interesting Mediterranean snakes. The ladder snake moves quickly and easily and is widespread in France and Spain. The strong four-lined ratsnake lives in the Balkans and Southern Italy. It reaches 7 feet (2 m) in length. In Europe, only the ringed snake and the moray eel of southern France, a snake-like fish that grows to a length of 8 feet (250 cm), are longer.

The short-toed eagle, a rare bird of prey, feeds almost exclusively on snakes and large lizards. When reptiles become scarce, so does the short-toed eagle. It is becoming

With a snake in its beak, a female short-toed eagle returns to its nest (opposite page: below, left) where a chick is waiting to be fed.

rarer since people are changing the land and reducing the bird's main prey, snakes. In southern Europe, the largest number of short-toed eagles lives in the western Mediterranean, with three thousand pairs in Spain and four hundred in France. It is not certain how many live in other countries.

Tortoises and Turtles

Land tortoises of the genus *Testudo,* the spur-tailed Mediterranean tortoise, and the spur-thighed Mediterranean tortoise are typical Mediterranean species. Very little is known about their habits and the way they behave. They live in places with a leafy-looking and shrubby cover, where they can easily hide and find food, mostly plants. They are usually found near waterways.

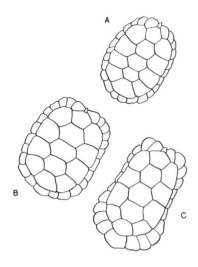

The tortoises, despite their famous slowness and heavy shells, are able to travel long distances. They sometimes travel over difficult routes, such as steep slopes and thick vegetation, searching for food or for a partner in the mating season. They prefer to go out in the not-too-hot hours and rest at night. During seasons of bad weather, they enter a dormant state, digging a hole in the ground in which to sleep away the season.

Tortoises are disappearing rapidly all over the world for several reasons: (1) being hit by traffic along the roads, (2) illegal buying and selling by dealers, and (3) dying in fires in the forests and maquis.

Few predators eat tortoises. Among those that do are the golden eagle, the Egyptian vulture, and the bearded vulture. The bearded vulture—now present mainly on the islands of Crete and Corsica—drops the tortoise from a high altitude and breaks its shell. According to tradition, the Greek poet Aeschylus is supposed to have died because a large bird of prey dropped a tortoise on his head.

Besides the three species of land tortoises, two freshwater turtles are found in the Mediterranean basin: the European swamp turtle and the *Mauremys caspica*, a striped-neck turtle. The first is found in the marshes and ponds of southern Europe. The *Mauremys caspica* is found in the Caspian Sea, as its name suggests, as well as all over North Africa and the Iberian and Balkan peninsulas.

In contrast to the land tortoises that feed mostly on plant substances, these freshwater turtles hunt for animal protein. Insects, tadpoles, mollusks, and small fish are easily caught in their jaws, thanks to their remarkable agility and speed in swimming. At the smallest sign of danger, they quickly dive and hide on the muddy bottom.

Like the land tortoises, these turtles are disappearing today, mostly because of the draining of wet areas. However, they are quite adaptable, and they still survive where vast marshes used to exist. These former marshes are now slow-moving drainage canals, rich in water plant life.

BIRDS OF
THE MAQUIS

The dense Mediterranean maquis is rich in fruit and flowers. These make life possible for a large number of insects and form an ideal environment for birds. Among these birds, the group richest in species is the songbirds. They are also possibly the most interesting because of the different ways in which they adapt to the environment. The most distinctive Mediterranean songbirds of the maquis are the warblers, little birds of the genus *Sylvia* (from the Latin *silva*, meaning "woods").

Sylviids

The Sylviids eat mainly insects. They have thin, pointed beaks and long tails for balance in acrobatic spins around small branches. About three-quarters of the species of the genus *Sylvia* nest somewhere in the Mediterranean region. The best known are the blackcap, the garden warbler, the Sardinian warbler, the Dartford warbler, and the white-throat. Almost half live only in the Mediterranean region. Some, like the Marmora's warbler and the Ruppell's warbler, are limited to a few large islands and to relatively isolated coastal areas in the region. The Sardinian warbler lives around the shores of the entire Mediterranean, in the same habitat as the olive tree. The Sardinian warbler could be considered the official symbol of that region.

The Sardinian warbler is one of the most common species in the dry Mediterranean garigue. There it looks for insects and berries, flying from one bush to another. Those who observe it, active and full of song in the hot Mediterranean summers, may ask how it can so easily tolerate the torrid climate. For now, only part of the answer is known: the black coloring of the head is a defense against the strong rays of the sun, like the dark hair of most Mediterranean people. The red eye ring—seen in other Mediterranean warblers—protects the eye from the bright light. The warbler can save water inside its body, much the same as desert animals.

The Sardinian warbler is also uniquely Mediterranean in its choice of habitat. It stays in bushes and shrubs and ventures away only to the lowest of olive tree branches. The tallest branches are left to other warblers such as the blackcap and the garden warbler. In a sparse holm oak grove with plenty of bushes and underbrush, a vertical distribution of the species can be seen. The blackcaps (and in spring, the garden warblers) will feed among the taller foliage, and the Sardinian warbler will look for food in the underbrush.

Opposite page: A stonechat is perched at the top of a young Corsican pine, a Mediterranean pine that is common in the basin along mountainous seacoasts. The stonechat is found all over Europe and migrates only as far as the southernmost parts of Europe and Africa.

43

Thus, they do not get in each other's way, and each species is able to gather enough food to survive.

Other Birds

The Mediterranean environments are, of course, visited by many other birds. But only a few can be considered truly characteristic of the region, and none of these species is more native to the maquis than the warblers.

The black-eared wheatear, the black wheatear, and the blue rock thrush prefer to live in rocky environments. The crested lark, the thekla lark, the calandra lark, the short-toed lark, the lesser short-toed lark, the European bee-eater, and the common roller prefer different levels of the steppes.

Among these birds, those of the skylark family (the crested lark, the calandra lark, and the short-toed lark) walk

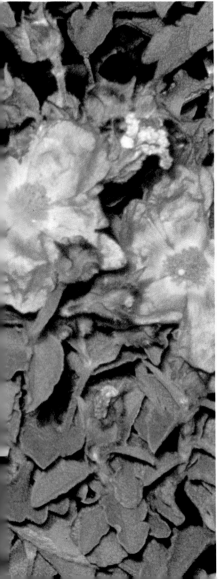

a great deal. To make walking easier, they have a long, straight toenail on the rear toe. Their colors blend well with their walking grounds: meadows, grain fields, and the sunburned stubble where they hide their nests.

The bee-eater and the roller, on the other hand, are among the most multicolored and flashy birds in Europe. The bee-eater nests in holes dug in banks of soil, and the roller nests in hollow trees in forests of oaks, pines, cedars, or other trees. They gather on electric lines, the bee-eater using the lines and the roller the poles as convenient diving boards for diving rapidly after insects.

Among the small fringillid finches, none is exclusive to the Mediterranean region, but some species are particularly at home here. The goldfinch is good at gathering thistle seed. The greenfinch and the serin also get along well in the pine forests and in the maquis environment.

Among the crows is the very beautiful azure-winged magpie, found only in Spain, Portugal, and thousands of miles away in eastern Asia. It is possible that this elegant bird was imported to the Iberian Peninsula by some ancient traveler.

Migration

The Mediterranean region is tucked between north-central Europe and Africa, between the areas of breeding and wintering of many bird species. It is, therefore, an area that migrating birds pass through—in autumn on the way from Europe to Africa, and in spring on the return trip.

The travel routes of these migrating birds are well planned. They must be safe and full of rest areas. Very few birds, for example, cross long tracts of open sea where it would be impossible to rest or feed. Migratory flocks generally travel along the peninsulas and use the islands to get closer to the continental coasts.

For these reasons, in the Mediterranean basin there are a few specific migration routes. Starting from west to east, there is first a route that begins at the Rif Mountains and at the Atlantic coast of Morocco. It passes through the Strait of Gibraltar and up toward the Iberian Peninsula. This path is chosen mainly by the birds breeding in north-central Europe, particularly in France, Germany, and Great Britain, in addition to those that breed in Spain or Portugal.

Two routes go through Italy, beginning south of the Atlas Mountains stretching from Morocco to Tunisia. Birds on these routes fly above the Tunisian peaks near Biserta

Above: A typical bird of the steppe, the European bee-eater is the only representative here of a family that is widely found in Africa and Asia. The male and female have identical plumage. With their beaks, the pair carves out a long tunnel and then builds the nest at the end.

Below: Migration routes from Africa and the Near East to Europe are traced. The return routes vary slightly.

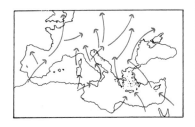

and Cape Bon and Pelagian Islands. One path then jumps to Sardinia and the other to Sicily.

The first route uses the Sardinian and Corsican ponds as rest stops. It has landing places on the Ligurian shores of Italy and the French Riviera, continuing over the plains and mountains of France and Italy. Some birds continue their journey up to the German plain through the Alps.

The route that includes Sicily follows instead a north-easterly direction. From Sicily, the birds pass to the south-central Tyrrhenian coasts of Italy. From here some birds continue north and stop to nest along the Italian peninsula. Most of the birds, however, follow the rivers down the middle of the Apennine passes, cross the Adriatic Sea, and land in the northern part of the Balkan Peninsula. From there they spread out toward south-central Europe, Russia, and Scandinavia.

Another migratory route involves only the Balkan

Peninsula. It originates on the coasts of Egypt and eastern Libya, and uses the Aegean islands and the Peloponesian peninsula as a bridge to the continent. Then it follows the peninsula, crossing Greece, Yugoslavia, and the plains of southern Europe.

A last route originates in the Middle East. It crosses Cyprus and the Anatolian peninsula, and reaches the plains of Bulgaria, Rumania, and southern Russia.

The migrations occur in spring and autumn. The routes are not necessarily the same coming and going. Migration is a spectacular sight to be seen at the straits, where millions of birds meet on their routes. At certain meeting points—over Gibraltar, the Sicilian Channel, the Strait of Messina, and the Bosphorus—large groups of birds can be seen passing through at certain times of the year: songbirds, birds of prey, wading birds, and others. In autumn and spring it is a tradition for bird-watchers to meet in Istanbul, Andalusia of southern Spain, and on Cape Bon to count birds of prey or storks.

The number of these birds can be amazing. Eleven thousand storks and 33,000 buzzards were counted passing a single point over the Bosporus. In Gibraltar, at the end of the summer of 1972, at least 39,000 kites were identified. On August 22, 13,356 were counted in just one day. Over Cape Bon, in two weeks during May 1975, over 8,000 honey buzzards were seen.

Unfortunately, these remarkable concentrations of birds also attract the attention of a few local bird hunters. They illegally bag the small birds on Cyprus and Malta and hunt honey buzzards on the Strait of Messina. These hunters are becoming fewer and fewer. They are holdovers from long ago when the Mediterranean people used migratory birds to supplement their poor diet. A few of the hunters who kill honey buzzards on the Strait of Messina do so out of fear and belief in ancient superstitions.

Wintering

The mildness of the winter climate and the presence of fruiting evergreen plants attract many nesting birds from central and southern Europe. Many species, arriving in autumn from the North, stop to spend the winter in the basin area rather than continuing to Africa.

Among these species are thrushes, Fringillid finches, common starlings, blackcaps, and willow warblers. These are also found south of the Sahara. Many of these birds feed

On these pages are some small birds measuring between 5 and 6 inches (13 and 15 cm) from beak to tail that populate the Mediterranean environment. Next to them, vegetation typical of the basin is shown. *From top to bottom and left to right:* olive tree warbler on common olive, Ruppell's warbler on olive-leaved daphne, Dartford warbler on a small branch of mastic tree, Marmora's warbler on oleander, serin feeding on the ground, Sardinian warbler on myrtle, *Agrobates galactotes* on the ground, and subalpine warbler on rosemary.

in olive groves. In fact, starlings make such a habit of this that they are very damaging for agriculture.

Other species migrate short distances, going from the mountain areas of the deciduous (green, leafy) woods to the truly Mediterranean coastal zones. Such is the case with the Eurasian robin, the Dunnock, the black redstart, the kinglets, and other birds. These species like to spend the winter in the Mediterranean maquis environments. In spring, they move only a short distance to nest in the woods of Spanish chestnut, oak, and European beech.

There are also many humid zones in the Mediterranean. These are excellent places for large groups of ducks, coots, herons, and gulls to spend the winter. Lately many studies have been made on ducks in particular, and today much more is known about the relative importance of the various wintering grounds of these birds. Lakes and coastal lagoons, river deltas, and marshes are especially welcoming to them, if not disturbed by hunters.

Bird Censuses

Birds are important ecological indicators. An ecological indicator is an organism so closely related to particular environmental conditions that the fact that an organism lives in a given place is proof that the related conditions exist there also. By knowing what kinds of birds live in a particular environment, ecologists can make some assumptions about the conditions of that environment.

Thus, a scientific study of an environment should include keeping track of the kinds of birds that live there. But there is another important factor to consider as well, that is, how many of each kind are present.

In the last few years, Mediterranean ecologists have lacked good methods and techniques for bird counting. Because maquis environments are so dense and hard to reach, certain counting methods that work well in other places don't work here. French ecologists adapted some of these methods to suit Mediterranean habitats.

There are two kinds of methods for counting birds: absolute and relative. Absolute methods indicate the actual density of pairs of birds per surface unit. Relative methods estimate how dense the population is compared to another area of land.

One type of absolute method is called the "mapping method." However, this method is not suitable for determining bird density in maquis environments. To use it, a complex grid of paths must be mapped out in an area tens of

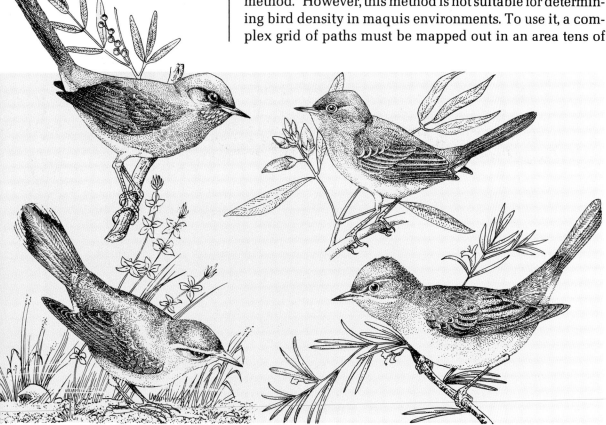

An azure-winged magpie stands next to a dwarf fan palm. This elegant bird, smaller than the magpie, is often found among the Mediterranean maquis of southern Spain.

thousands of square feet wide. An observer then visits the mapped area during the breeding period, when male birds sing to attract mates. The observer walks along the paths about ten different times in order to determine the exact location of the males heard singing. The observer then marks the birds' locations on the grid. This method cannot be used in the maquis environment because the vegetation is too thick. It is impossible to create a grid of paths along which an observer could easily walk.

Another method, called a "linear itinerary," is more suitable. In this method, an observer covers a path several miles long during the breeding season, and marks the location of all singing males on a map. As a result, a few groups of birds are counted in the same spots, really representing the same bird or breeding pair heard or seen more than once. Because the path being tracked is straight, the count doesn't give the population density directly.

To estimate the real density, the average bird count of this particular environment could be compared to another that was easier to count. Therefore, this is a relative method of estimating population density.

However, even the linear itinerary method isn't always possible or useful in Mediterranean environments. In such cases, the last resort is the point method. By providing a reasonably accurate estimate of the bird population density, the point method produces the same results as the mapping method.

The point method is based upon listening to singing males for twenty minutes in each of a series of fixed listening stations inside a homogenous (same) environment. The counts recorded provide an estimate of how many birds live there, but do not describe very well the areas in which each species of bird lives. They do, however, reflect the frequency of each species in a given habitat. French ornithologists have shown an expected connection between frequency and abundance of the species. In other words, if a bird is present in ten out of ten stations, it can be considered abundant.

The point method has solved quite a few problems for ornithologists. Using the results of thirty or forty point surveys, quick estimates can be made for qualitative (kinds) and quantitative (numbers) studies of the bird life in environments that are hard to reach. Researchers can then use this information for wildlife management and nature conservation.

Diagram of a bird's body

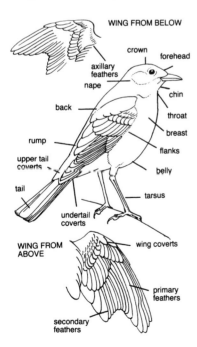

WING FROM BELOW

crown
forehead
axillary
feathers
nape
chin
back
throat
breast
rump
flanks
upper tail
coverts
belly
tail
tarsus
undertail
coverts
WING FROM
ABOVE
wing coverts
primary
feathers
secondary
feathers

A blue throat is about to be released after banding. Recently around the Mediterranean, national parks, universities, and private organizations have set up ornithological stations to observe bird life. It is hoped that these research centers will expand people's knowledge of all the birds that visit the Mediterranean region throughout the year.

Ornithological Observations

To better understand breeding, migration, or wintering, field stations are needed to continuously observe the various species of birds. Whenever possible, some birds should be marked so that researchers who might find them elsewhere will recognize them.

Many such stations have been operating for many years in the countries of central and western Europe. They have allowed a lot to be learned about ornithology. In the Mediterranean region, however, people have only recently become interested in ornithology. So there are not as many bird tracking stations there.

One of these stations is on the island of Vivara, in the Gulf of Naples. It was founded in 1980 by a group of zoologists (scientists who study animals) from the University of Naples. The 79-acre (32-hectare) island is connected to neighboring Procida Island by a bridge, but no people live there. It is covered with a rich maquis of strawberry trees

This ornithological station is the Palo, located on the Tyrrhenian coast of Latium, Italy. Here, birds that have just been caught are placed in small cloth bags, one per bag. The researcher records their weight, size, and fat content. From this data, where the birds come from and the purpose of their flights are determined.

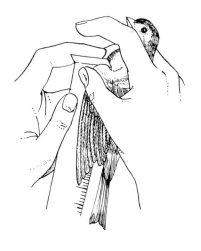

and evergreen shrubs of erica and myrtle. There are also some abandoned olive groves. Japanese flying nets have been set up to allow for the capturing, banding, and releasing of thousands of small birds every year.

The work of the researchers is done mostly in the spring, when many birds stop to rest for a short time on the small island as they return to their northern breeding grounds. All the captured birds are marked with a little band that carries an international abbreviation showing where the bird was banded. The birds are also weighed, measured, and recorded in a register.

The researchers are notified of any recapture of the banded birds by other European observers. For example, a male black redstart (a little gray bird with a brick-red tail) weighing about a half-ounce (18 grams) was banded on Vivara on February 25, 1982. It was recaptured on March 25 near Bielsko-Biala, in southern Poland. This is about 620 miles (1,000 km) in a straight line from the release point.

Thus, information is gathered on movements of birds in the European continent, the length of their lives, the birth and death rates, the size of their populations, and the changes in the population size. This information helps scientists to better understand how nature works, and insures a better life not only for the birds, but for people, too.

Above: The diagrams show how a bird's wing is measured and how a band is fastened to its leg. *Right:* A bird's beak is measured using the compass method. The little bird shown is a spotted flycatcher measuring about 5 to 5.5 inches (13 to 14 cm) long. It nests in forks of branches or on walls covered with climbing vegetation or shrubs.

MAMMALS

Ungulates

The class of hoofed mammals called ungulates generally refers to the antelope of the African savannas, the red deer of the European forests, and the elk and reindeer of the cold forests of North America and Europe. However, some species of these herbivorous (plant-eating) animals also live in the Mediterranean basin. Not only are they rare, but they are also shy and difficult to observe.

Mature forests with little underbrush are the favorite environment of the fallow deer, a cervid (having antlers) mammal. The average fallow deer measures 30 inches (80 cm) tall and is 55 inches (140 cm) long. The male weighs more than 220 pounds (100 kilograms). The fallow deer lives in small herds of either adult males or adult females with their young.

The color of the coat varies with the seasons. In winter, it is dark chestnut brown with a grayish cast. It changes in spring to a much lighter reddish brown, spotted with white.

The whole rear end and tail has the shape of an upside-down anchor, and this has a special function. The position of the tail in respect to the rump serves as a signal to the rest of the herd. A tail waving back and forth is a sign of peace. A tail not moving and pointing downward signals a minor alarm. A tail lifted halfway indicates that the animal is on the look-out. A completely lifted tail signals a grave danger and warns the rest of the herd to flee.

The mating season comes in autumn. After having spent spring and summer filling up on leaves, buds, fruit of the underbrush, acorns, grain, and legumes, the animals dedicate themselves to fighting and mating. On October days, in the few Mediterranean locations where ungulates are found, the males can be heard bellowing or seen colliding with one another. Making loud, deep sounds is the ungulates' way of warning each other to keep away from the individual territories to which they lay claim.

Gestation (pregnancy) lasts about eight months and births occur beginning in May. Within forty-eight hours of birth, the fawn is already able to follow its mother. The tines (pointed parts) of the new antlers begin to appear at around nine months of age, and the velvety skin protecting them is shed shortly after thirteen months. The antlers fall off every year and grow back again the following spring.

The fallow deer are indigenous, or native, to Asia Minor, Palestine, and Lebanon. They were probably brought to Europe by the Phoenicians and the Romans. Although

Opposite page: Clearly visible on the back of this specimen is the white "saddle" that is a trademark of the male mouflon's winter coat. This marking is found only on purer species.

57

Some meat-eating animals, or carnivores, that live in the Mediterranean have developed unique characteristics. Some examples are the spotted lynx (of which only a few remain) that inhabits Spain, the genet that is found in France and on the Iberian Peninsula, and the ichnoumon of the Iberian Peninsula, Dalmatia, and the Circeo promontory. The spotted lynx is a much-feared predator. Up to 3.5 feet (110 cm) long and 23 to 27 inches (60 to 70 cm) high at the shoulder, it feeds mainly on rabbits and competes with the European wildcat for the same prey. The genet, unmistakable by its long ringed tail, and the ichneumon are the only European examples of the two subfamilies known as Herpestinae and Viverrinae. Those animals are widespread in Africa and Asia. Both are hunters of Eurasian common shrews, dormice, and small birds.

they used to be common in the European forests, the fallow deer suffered in the snowy climate. Now they are only found in rare Mediterranean coastal forests.

Though now rare and localized, red deer still live today in a few Mediterranean forests. In Tunisia and on the island of Sardinia, a few of two particular subspecies survive: *Cervus elaphus barbarus* and *Cervus elaphus corsicanus.* Elsewhere, as at Coto Doñana and the woods of Mesola, the Mediterranean deer generally appear rather small compared to the red deer of central Europe. Their life habits are similar to those of the fallow deer. This deer has many mates but lives only with herds of its own gender (male or female) outside the mating period. In North America, the same species is called the North American elk.

The mouflon is another distinctive Mediterranean species, native to the forests of holm oak and cork in Sardinia and Corsica. It is the smallest subspecies of the wild sheep. The male is 30 inches (80 cm) tall and 50 inches (120 cm) long, and weighs about 65 pounds (30 kg). It has spiral horns facing downward. The female usually has no horns, though she may have short horns. The color of the male coats is chestnut-brown, while the females have lighter coats.

The mating season is autumn, a period in which the competition and battles among the males for the females are intense. The rest of the year, the sexes live separately. The males roam alone, and the females gather in small herds. The fawns weigh about 5.5 pounds (2.5 kg), and in a short three days' time, they can follow their mothers.

The wild goat leads a quiet, reserved life among the maquis and the garigue of some islands and mountain chains of the Mediterranean. It is similar to the wild goat of the Alps and Pyrenees mountains. The most predictable populations of those goats considered wild are found on the islands of Crete and perhaps Yioura in the northern Sporades east of Greece. Elsewhere, as at Montecristo, east of Italy, and Andimilo, north of Crete, domestic goats that have become wild are found instead. Since the wild goats are spread throughout each island and isolated from other islands, each area has developed its own special race.

The males stand 27 inches (69 cm) high, 27 inches (69 cm) long, and weigh about 90 pounds (40 kg). At this size, they are slightly larger than the females. Their horns are

Two young red deer cross a pond in Coto Doñana. A common ungulate, the deer is widespread in the whole world from North Africa to Siberia. The Mediterranean breed is slightly smaller and is most often found in the deltas.

long, not branched, and shaped like curved swords with the points facing backward. The females also have horns, which are much smaller. The color of their coats is generally chestnut brown, but varies within a population. The goats live in unisex (male or female only) herds. The males and females meet only during the September mating season. The offspring, or kids, are born in February, after a gestation of about five months.

Mediterranean wild goats spend their lives climbing and jumping among the rocks, looking for bushes of their favorite foods, erica and rosemary. They also feed on young

shoots and plants of many other species. This means that no vegetation in the woods ever has a chance to grow very much before being eaten. This is the case on the island of Montecristo, where the goat population prevents the development of the holm oak. A holm oak environment is only found in a few hard-to-reach island zones.

The average life of a goat depends on where it lives. The goats of Montecristo live eleven to twelve years, while some living in the Aegean region reach fifteen to seventeen years.

Rodents

In 1963, after a long investigation, the German naturalist Gunther Niethammer concluded that the crested porcupine is not an indigenous species of Italy and the Balkan countries but that it must have been brought to these countries by the Romans. There are still doubts about where the porcupine came from. Whether or not the Romans introduced it, the fact is that the porcupine, a native species of west and north Africa, thrived in Sicily, south-central Italy, and in some areas of the Balkan Peninsula.

Even though it can weigh as much as 33 pounds (15 kg), the crested porcupine is not easy to spot. It is easier to track its presence by the traces it leaves: quills that fall along the paths, and feces, shaped like small elongated balls. The porcupine lives in any number of different environments. It can live from the plains and hill areas (even those that are partially cultivated), to the mountain slopes, up to 3,300 ft (1,000 m) above sea level. It is also found from the areas of Mediterranean maquis to bushes, red-water tree (an African tree with poisonous bark) woods, and river and stream valleys. It is frequently found in quarries and where there are natural systems of caves. The porcupine is an excellent digger, able to enlarge natural holes with its powerful claws, and build deep, underground dens with a network of passages.

This shy and sullen rodent has not been studied much until now. It feeds on tubers, roots, fruit, grain, and other vegetation. It often gnaws the trunks and bark of trees. It makes no sounds except some grunts and hisses when it is angry. The meaning of some of its signals is still unknown, such as the way it makes its quills stand up and stamps the ground with its hind feet. When it is in danger, the porcupine turns its back to the enemy and sticks out its long, rear quills, puffing itself up and meanly shaking its tail. In

Pictured is a cross section of a crested porcupine's den. These complex underground excavations have various "rooms" for the adults, and other, more secluded rooms that are used for raising young. There can be three or four entrances and exits for the dens, or as many as twenty-five. This way, the crested porcupine has many escape hatches to elude the attacks of its many predators.

Europe, the porcupine's only enemies are probably humans.

The porcupine is nocturnal, which means it is awake only when it is dark. It has a sharp sense of smell and moves quite easily considering its size. During the winter, porcupines become lazy and sleepy and only come out on the warmest nights. Porcupines live alone or in family groups that generally break up when the young achieve independence. They reproduce at the beginning of spring. After a gestation of about two months, usually from one to three babies are born. At birth, the quills are soft, but they become dangerous in a few days. Babies become independent within three months.

The wild rabbit is perhaps the most widespread rodent in the Mediterranean. Its adaptability to rough habitats makes it a target for hunters even on the most arid little island. The survival of the wild rabbit depends on its ability to dig underground passageways, which may be complicated and twisted. Wild rabbits live in these passageways in colonies.

The wild rabbit is usually shy during the day. If disturbed or in danger, it quickly runs away. It can be spotted as it escapes, zig-zagging away as fast as it can with its little white tail pointed up. Generally, the wild rabbit is active during the night, at dusk, and at dawn.

This large rodent can weigh as much as 2.5 pounds (1 kg). The wild rabbit has many predators, and its only defense is to produce many offspring. In recent decades, a viral disease called myxomatosis has killed off many wild rabbits in some Mediterranean areas.

The Barbary Ape

On the mountains of Morocco and Algeria, and in Gibraltar, lives the Barbary ape. This ape is a member of the order Primates, the highest order of mammals, which includes tree shrews, monkeys, and humans. Barbary apes were probably brought to Europe by the Arabs. Those living in Gibraltar live almost as tame a life-style as their brothers and sisters in a zoo. But the Barbary ape remains the only wild monkey of the western Palaearctic region, which includes Europe, northern Asia, Arabia, and Africa. It is not a large animal. Adult males grow as tall as 28 inches (70 cm) and weigh as much as 22 lbs (10 kg).

An adult crested porcupine is surprised as it leaves its den to search for food. Tubers, bulbs, and roots are the essential diet needs of this animal. It also feeds on fruit fallen from trees and gnaws on their bark and trunks.

EAGLES AND VULTURES

Because of their great size, their spectacular forms, and their position at the top of the food chain, eagles and vultures have always fascinated those who have observed them. However, natural breeding areas for these animals grow fewer each year. The survival of these species will depend on the efforts of conservationists who now seek ways to protect them.

Eagles

The imperial eagle has already disappeared from North Africa and is near extinction in Europe. Only about eighty pairs of these birds are believed to remain throughout the world. Most of them are found in the Iberian Peninsula and eastern Europe. However, because eagles in Asia have mated with those remaining in eastern Europe, the process of extinction has slowed somewhat.

This eagle builds its nest on large isolated trees that stand from 20 to 65 feet (6 to 20 m) high. Between the end of February and the middle of March, it lays two to three, and in rare instances, four eggs. The eagle sits on them to warm them for forty-three days. After the eaglets (young eagles) are born, they remain in the nest for about two and a half months. Near the end of June or the beginning of July, they fly for the first time.

The Bonelli's eagle is a bird of prey that is adapted to life in the Mediterranean ecosystems (communities of plants and animals that interact within their respective environments). This elusive species is difficult to spot in the wild. However, it can be recognized by its distinctive white lower body parts that are dotted with black in the adult, its dark wing surface, and its large, powerful claws.

In Europe, including the Iberian Peninsula, France, Sardinia, Sicily, and Greece, it is estimated that a total of about two hundred pairs exist. In some areas of Europe, this species is considered to be endangered.

This decline is largely due to the change in the ecosystem, or the balance of nature. Also, the number of eagles is dropping because of illegal hunting by collectors who have them mounted and displayed.

Scientists have found that in the Mediterranean ecosystems, the season of the year influences what the Bonelli's eagle will prey on. In other words, it catches whatever animal is available at the time. The Bonelli's eagle occupies an ecological niche that is also occupied by the golden eagle.

Opposite page: A young Spanish imperial eagle is caught in its nest with the remains of its last prey (a wild rabbit). It has yet to develop the two large white wing patches it will get as an adult. The population of the imperial eagle in Spain and Portugal, considered by some scientists a species all its own, is very isolated. There are now only thirty to fifty pairs, 25 percent of these in the Guadalquivir marshes. The Spanish imperial eagle is threatened with extinction because of the destruction of its forest habitat. The forests have been changed through reforesting of blue gum and pine trees. The eagles are also in danger from the use of poisoned bait and pesticides, other disturbances from humans, and frequent fires.

Unmistakable for the beautiful color of its coat—dark brown tending to reddish on the back, off-white on the belly, and black on the snout—and its long tail shaped like a brush, the small garden dormouse is very common to the Mediterranean maquis. It is also one of the area's most common prey. It can be from 8 to 12 inches (20 to 30 cm) long, including the tail. A nocturnal animal, it easily climbs on trees. It feeds on vegetation, especially acorns and chestnuts, but never turns down a chance to prey on insects, snails, bird eggs, and nestlings.

The Bonelli's eagle begins breeding around the middle of February. It builds its nest on hard-to-reach rocky walls and normally lays two eggs or in rare cases, three. The eggs hatch from thirty-seven to forty days later, near the end of March. However, the eaglets do not leave the nest until late May or early June. This eagle tends to stay in one territory, although individuals, usually young or immature ones, have been observed migrating or wandering.

Vultures: The Problem of Food

Vultures are necrophagous birds, meaning that they feed on the carcasses of dead animals. Vultures find carcasses by sight only. Rooks, carrion crows, and red kites are also necrophagous birds, and vultures may notice these smaller birds near a carcass. But they do not depend totally on the smaller birds for clues. Before approaching a carcass, vultures look for unmistakable signs that the animal is dead, such as its belly having been slashed open by foxes.

A hierarchy, or an order, exists among the species that feed on a carcass. Generally, the large griffon vultures are first. They cover many miles in their search for food, especially when food is scarce, as in winter. The griffon vulture is the most aggressive. The smaller Egyptian vulture generally stays on the sidelines and feeds only when the griffon vultures are full. But the Egyptian attacks the carcass before the smaller species such as red kites and rooks. Next, the European black vultures arrive one by one on the carcass. They are less aggressive but larger than the griffon vultures. When there is more than one black vulture, the order of feeding within the group probably depends, as in the case of griffon vultures, on which is most aggressive. Finally, it is the bearded vultures' turn to feed. By this time, only the bones are left. Even so, this species of bird benefits from the protein that it gains from that food source.

Stock-rearing, the breeding of animals for profit, is one of the most important sources of income of people in the Mediterranean countries. From an ecological point of view, the massive introduction of domestic herbivores (plant-eating animals) has created an imbalance. Flocks and herds are found in most areas, and their constant grazing has caused vegetation to become scarce. Also, when these animals die out in the open, their carcasses draw vultures. This has happened so often that there are far more vultures than there would have been without the presence of the farmers' herds. This is especially true of griffon vultures. In

The small collar of woolly feathers, and a head and neck covered by compact white down, make the griffon the most "beautiful" of the vultures.

some countries, these large birds have depended on people and their labors for centuries.

But today the situation has reversed itself. Vultures are now facing a shortage of this food source because modern methods of breeding animals have helped to reduce the number of cattle that die before the farmers slaughter them. Another danger resulting from the work of humans threatens the vultures' existence. Farmers try to destroy rats, insects, and other threats to their crops by leaving poisoned meat and grain for them to eat. These practices have actually killed all vultures in some parts of the Mediterranean.

During this century, for example, the number of griffon vultures in Sardinia has quickly declined from one thousand to about one hundred. A rapid decrease or total extinction has also occurred in other countries.

When an animal becomes extinct, it leaves a tragic

A griffon vulture flies over a
Mediterranean wood. A great glider, it is
easily able to cover the long distances
necessary to find food.

A closeup of the lammergeier is provided. It used to be called the "lamb vulture," but ornithologists decided to change its name when they proved it does not feed on large animals, but instead on marrow bones, or turtles, which it thinks are bones to be picked. Because of this habit it is almost extinct. It is still widespread on the Himalayan and the Ethiopian plateaus. In the Mediterranean, it is reduced to a few tens of specimens concentrated in Corsica and Crete. Thanks to extraordinary agility and speed, this bird of prey is able to steal the prey of the golden eagle in midflight.

void. If the animal was especially well known because of its size, its disappearance becomes a sad symbol of what can happen in nature. This is how the griffon vulture is thought of now in some Mediterranean countries. There has been only one known case in which humans have reintroduced a species that had disappeared. This happened in the Cevennes Mountains of France.

On the south-central edge of the French Massif Central mountain range, the number of griffon vultures had dwindled by 1921. They were rarely seen flying in the skies. At that time, an attempt was made to save them by slaughtering animals and giving the carcasses to the vultures. In spite of those efforts, the vultures continued on the road to extinc-

Egyptain vulture

imperial eagle

bearded vulture

black vulture

griffon vulture

Bonelli's eagle

Flight silhouettes of large birds of prey and carrion-eaters living in the Mediterranean are shown. Among them, the most recognizable is the lammergeier, because of its long pointed wings and tail. *Left to right:* Egyptian vulture; black vulture; imperial eagle; griffon vulture; lammergeier; Bonelli's eagle

tion. Hunters continued to kill them, and they could find little food on which to survive. Finally, in 1968, a reintroduction effort was launched. No one had ever tried this before.

First, zoos and the Spanish government were asked to provide a few vultures for the experiment. At the same time, conservationists set up an area in which they kept a constant supply of carcasses of slaughtered animals, hoping that the birds would visit it for their food supply. The vultures were kept in aviaries, or bird sanctuaries, that looked out on the same steep mountainsides where they had nested long ago. To make the location even more familiar, mountain climbers dropped to some narrow ledges on the mountainside and painted the area white, to look like the fecal droppings of other griffon vultures.

Finally, in December 1981, the aviaries, containing thirty-five vultures, were opened. Some of these griffon vultures had been kept in captivity for over ten years so they waited a few days before deciding to test their new-found freedom. At first, they all stayed near the aviaries. But soon they scattered over an area of 200 sq. miles (500 sq. km).

Within a month, the vultures formed a flock. Then an amazing event occurred. They colonized the same mountainside that they had inhabited until the 1920s. One pair tried to mate, but they did not successfully build a nest. The food supply set up was by this time being visited regularly by all members of the flock. By the end of February and the beginning of March in 1982, two other pairs of vultures produced one egg each. Of these two eggs, only one hatched, but it was the beginning of a success.

ROCKY COASTS

Throughout the Mediterranean area, the rocky coastal areas still possess the most natural characteristics and shelter the most unusual animal and plant life. They are also the most inaccessible areas to people.

On the rocky coasts of the sea are plants like the samphire, the Mediterranean sea lavender, the silver groundsel, and the showy knapweed. Higher up are plants that are less resistant to salt, sometimes including native species. Among the most frequent plants are sweet scabious, varieties of pink dianthus, evergreen candytuft, and rosemary. These types of wild plants are characterized by their softly colored flowers. At the point where the low-growing maquis start, the most frequent plants are of the genus *Euphorbia*.

Considering how difficult these rocky coasts are to reach, it is not surprising that seabirds and cliff-dwelling birds are the animals usually found in this habitat. Among these birds are gulls, green cormorants, Cory's shearwaters, peregrine falcons, and Eleonora's falcons.

Mediterranean Herring Gull

Herring gulls, which inhabit a widespread area, differ somewhat in appearance from one area to another. The overall color of these birds is a variety of shades of gray. The legs may be pink or yellow and the primary flight feathers show different designs. Because of these differences, herring gulls don't look much alike.

Herring gulls are typical inhabitants of the Mediterranean rocky coasts and are the most common sea gulls of the basin. They build their nests high on cliffs with wide shelves, little ledges, and typical rock vegetation.

Though it moves often during winter, this large and graceful gull returns to its colony by February or March when the breeding season starts. A great deal is known about its behavior, mainly because of the Dutch ornithologist Nikolaas Tinbergen, who was educated in England and eventually won a Nobel Prize in biology.

One of Tinbergen's important discoveries was finding out the significance of the characteristic red spot on the herring gull's lower mandible, or jaw. When the chick is hungry, it pecks the adult on this red spot several times until the adult opens its mouth and gives the chick some regurgitated food. That is, the adult chews, swallows, and then brings the partially digested food back into its mouth to feed to the chick. Clearly, this red spot is an important part of the communication between the adults and the chicks.

Opposite page: A high rocky coast with *Euphorbia dendroides* is pictured. Like the rocky coasts of the Atlantic, the Mediterranean also offers nesting sites suited to many species of birds. The dense flocks so typical of the Atlantic aren't found here, however.

Audouin's gull doesn't fit any particular environment harmoniously, and is only found here and there in isolated spots. It feeds almost exclusively on fish, but in the spring and summer, it also catches insects and small mammals. It breeds in the middle of April. Its present population, probably lower than five thousand pairs, is mainly concentrated in Greece, Morocco, Sardinia, and the Baleares Islands.

Audouin's Gull

Among the large birds, the Audouin's gull is an interesting example of a species that can only be found in one area. It makes its home only in the Mediterranean.

The rare Audouin's gull is smaller in size than the herring gull, but the color of the feathers of the two birds is similar, especially in the adult. The easiest way to recognize the Andouin's gull is by its colorful beak. It is red at the base, banded with black in the middle, and yellow at the point.

Shag

The shag, or green cormorant, belongs to the order Pelicaniformes, or pelican. It develops a crest during the breeding season. Like most seabirds, it has developed special features that allow it to fish under the water. Shags have elongated bodies, long necks, hooked beaks, webbed feet, and short wings. The Mediterranean shag, which is known for its small crest, does not wander far from its home.

Shags nest in colonies and begin to nest early in winter. Because people have taken over part of the shag's territory, it nests in fewer locations. In spite of this, the species can still be found throughout the Mediterranean.

Cory's Shearwater

This bird of the order Procellariiformes is widely distributed in the Mediterranean area. Some populations are also being found on islands in the Atlantic Ocean such as the Canary Islands, the Azores, the Selvagens Islands, and those near Cape Verde. All Procellariiformes are birds of the high seas and usually come to land only to reproduce.

Researchers who have studied the biology of the Cory's shearwater on the Selvagens and the island of Paximadhia south of Crete have collected a great deal of information. However, it is still not known what fraction of the population winters in the Mediterranean.

The male and female have different songs and sing long duets. At the end of May, the female lays one pure white egg that is very elongated. The nest is built on the ground where it is sheltered by pebbles and shrubs. The mates sit on the egg in the nest, each taking turns that last several days for a total of fifty-four days. About the middle of July, the chick is born.

For the first six to eight weeks, this slow-growing chick is given a daily diet of fish and cephalopods such as squid. The adult feeds the chick by regurgitating food. Later, the adults feed the chicks once every three days, and they begin to grow rapidly. By mid-September, the chicks weigh 70 percent of its adult weight. Still later, as the feathers grow, the supply of accumulated fat will be exhausted. Finally, in October, the birds abandon the nest.

The colony is made up of adults and immature members who were born in the same nesting place, are less than five years old, and are not yet able to breed. Usually located in inaccessible areas or on tiny islands, these colonies can range from a few individuals to more than ten

thousand pairs. This species returns faithfully to the same nesting place each year. Researchers have tracked pairs that returned to the same nest for eleven consecutive breeding seasons. The oldest individual found in a colony was sixteen years old. To gather this information, researchers used the banding method of tracking the birds.

The Cory's shearwater has a keen sense of direction and probably uses the stars and the sun as points of reference. In an experiment, two males were taken at the end of May from a den on the remote island of Linosa, located in the Mediterranean Sea south of Sicily. They were flown to a place near Palermo in northwest Sicily. After about twelve hours in captivity, they were freed. They immediately flew in the right direction, that is, east towards Trapani. One was found in its nest within twenty-four hours and the other within forty-eight.

Peregrine Falcon

Called an "ecological barometer" by the ornithologist Jan Newton, the peregrine falcon was almost wiped out because of chemical pollutants. For this reason, this bird of prey has been the object of much attention. This falcon preyed on small birds that ate insects. These insects contained trace amounts of the insecticide DDT. The DDT became concentrated in the falcon's bloodstream, causing death or sterility. Unable to reproduce, these birds almost disappeared in northern Europe in the 1950s and 1960s. The species began to return only after the insecticide was banned.

In the Mediterranean, according to the most recent investigations, the peregrine falcon population did decrease but now remains quite stable. It lives on rocky coasts, and on inaccessible inland cliffs. Peregrines stay near a favorite roosting site, and their behavior follows regular patterns. They have a short nesting season that begins in late February or early March. The young birds begin to leave the nest by the beginning of May.

As is common for birds of prey, there is a division of labor during nesting. The larger female sits on the nest and feeds the chicks, leaving for only short periods. The male is responsible for catching prey, which it does with incredible ability. Once it locates the prey, generally a bird of average or small size, the falcon catches it from above with a breathtaking dive. It strikes the prey with its claws, not with the chest, as was once believed.

Opposite page: Pictured is a distribution of birds on the rocky coast, depending on the various heights. On the "highest planes" are found the insect-eating birds and those eating on the ground. Examples of these are rock doves *(top, above left)*, a favorite prey of the peregrine falcon, and the blue rock thrush *(bottom, above left).* On the "high planes," ready to take flight and dive, are the birds of prey that find their favorite prey in the other birds up there. Drawing, *above center:* a peregrine falcon perching; *above right:* Eleonora's falcon flying. At lower altitudes fly birds that find their food in the sea and therefore hover above it. From top to bottom: Cory's shearwater, with its chick in a den dug in the ground; some herring gulls; a pair of shags, one in a nest built of dry twigs and algae.

Eleonora's Falcon

Very little was known about the Eleonora's falcon until 1961 when an English ornithologist first studied it. That study provided the first information about the life and habitat of this unusual bird of prey. Since then, other researchers have become interested in this falcon.

Eleonora's falcons live in colonies. The majority nest in the Mediterranean, though there are some that build their nests on the Atlantic coasts of Morocco and the Canary Islands. They winter in Madagascar in the Indian Ocean. Each year, a total of about sixty-seven thousand pairs, make this long migration twice. The first time they fly to the Madagascar area, and in the spring they make a second trip, returning to their nesting spots. These locations are either cliffs near isolated rocky coasts or small islands. At this time, it is easy to catch sight of these birds. They have long tails and falconlike pointed wings. They prey on both flying and ground insects, using hunting techniques that are similar to the circling of the common kestrel, a small falcon that hovers in the air against the wind.

The Eleonora's falcon breeds late and has not begun to breed even by the beginning of summer. Finally, at the end of July, it lays two or three eggs that hatch between the middle and the end of August. As these chicks are growing, many small birds such as songbirds travel nearby on their autumn migration. They become easy prey for the falcons.

A young peregrine falcon perches on a rocky ledge. Egg-raiders of the nesting areas of this and other species take advantage of the brief moments the female is away from the nest. This forces naturalists to keep strict watch on the nests until the eggs hatch. The chicks born from artificially incubated eggs are sold to unscrupulous collectors.

78

The hunt usually occurs in the morning, often along the coast. They hunt in groups, and each falcon is able to catch many small birds and bring them to the nest. Within a month, the nestlings begin flying and are weaned gradually. Finally, in October, all the falcons, young and adults, begin their long voyage to the wintering zones of Madagascar.

Blue Rock Thrush

A famous songbird, the male of the blue rock thrush is characterized by an elegant blue coat. Slightly smaller than a blackbird, this member of the Turdinae subfamily visits the highest cliffs. There the common vegetation is thick *Euphorbia* bushes and shrubby plants of the low maquis. In most cases, the blue thrush chooses a high, jutting rock on which to land and, from there, sings its sweet song which in spring becomes even more melodious.

The female is more timid and has darker, grayish feathers. Female songbirds usually do not sing, and this is true of the female blue rock thrush as well. In spring, it builds a nest that is usually placed in a rock crevice. Both partners care for the offspring, feeding them insects and larger prey, such as small lizards. Though easily observed on the rocky coasts of the Mediterranean, the thrush is seen less away from the sea. Well into the continent, it disappears completely.

A flying Eleonora's falcon is pictured. Besides this light-colored form, with its lower parts striped in brown and red, another kind is completely dark-colored. The Italian name was given to this small bird of prey in honor of Eleonora d'Arborea. She was a regent and judge in Sardinia who decided these falcons deserved special protection. In 1392, she made an official decree called the *Carta de loga*.

DELTAS
AND COASTAL
MARSHES

The main effect that rivers have on the coast is that they carry soil, sand, and other fine particles called "silt" and deposit them on the coast. This process, known as "sedimentation," is a benefit since the coastal area is not large. There are major rivers that flow into the Mediterranean where they form deltas, (silt deposits at the mouths of rivers) or lakes and marshes along the coast. These major rivers are the Ebro in Spain, the Rhone in France, and the Po in Italy.

Other rivers are the Neretva and the Moraca in Yugoslavia, the waterways of the Seman in Albania from Karavestas to the lagoon of Nartes and the Acheloos in Greece which includes the marshes of Mesolóngion. The Axios River in Southern Yugoslavia and northern Greece and its neighboring rivers, the Mesta and the Evros, flow into the Mediterranean also.

Two other typical marshy environments have Mediterranean climates but do not actually flow into the Mediterranean basin. These are at the mouths of the Guadalquivir River in Spain and the Danube River in Romania. The first flows into the Atlantic Ocean west of Gibraltar, and the second into the Black Sea.

The Environments

These wetlands can be found easily along the seacoast. However, the amount of land that they cover varies in size, and some are more polluted than others.

Along beaches where clusters of shorebirds gather, there are dunes created by winds that have formed hills and valleys in the sand. Varieties of shorebirds such as plovers, oystercatchers, and stone curlews live there. Interesting species can be observed in the Doñana Reserve, at the mouth of the Guadalquivir River. Plants such as the strawberry-tree and juniper are there in abundance. Behind the dunes, the short-toed eagle rules over the pine forests. Other creatures that thrive in this area are the buzzard, wood pigeon, Lataste's viper, and tortoises.

Visitors can also glimpse the blue-green flash of the common kingfisher bird as it dives for fish or, perhaps, as it swiftly escapes a pursuing falcon. A larger variety of kingfisher, called the lesser pied kingfisher, appears in the Egyptian lagoons.

Some of these lake areas, in particular the Camargue in France, the delta of the Ebro, and Mesolóngion, have become salt pans—shallow coastal areas where the salty seawater flows in and quickly evaporates, leaving salt de-

Opposite page: A young cattle egret stands next to a cow. Among the herons, it is the least aquatic species. It has learned to live far from the wetlands, joining the herds of large herbivores that provide it with food by lifting insects from the ground with their hooves. Thanks to this adaptation it has spread widely, moving from Africa to Europe and to South and (eventually) North America.

Above: A flying purple heron is pictured. This member of the *Ardeidae* family is tied to the marshy zones, and often nests among the canebrakes. Of all the herons it is the least common. In the adult specimens, rusty tones predominate on the neck and the belly. Their backs are a reflective gray-blue. Their necks and chests have dark lines and dots. The nape feathers are black and the legs reddish.

Opposite page: The bearded tit is so called because of its two black moustaches on the sides of its beak. It is a songbird that lives only in the marshy zones. The coypu or nutria whose outline is shown swimming on the surface of the water is a rodent indigenous to South America with a valued fur. It is mainly an aquatic creature and is now seen all over Europe since many of them escaped from breeding stock.

posits. As a result, some bird species that used to nest there no longer can survive in the new environment and have left.

Other animals populate tiny islands or sandy beaches where groves of trees have grown. On the Doñana Nature Reserve, some rare species are found among the cork tree woods. For instance, the lynx, the small-spotted genet, the ringed snake, and a type of imperial eagle are unusual species that live in this reserve.

In contrast, Eurasian river otter, European mink, and raccoon dogs from distant China are some of the animals that thrive in the delta of the Danube River, located on the north shore of the Black Sea. These species prefer the woods near Sakhalin Island. Amphibians such as the tree frog, (*Hyla arborea*), the red-bellied howler (*Bombina bombina*), and the green frog (*Rana psulenta*) are also suited to the environment at the mouth of the Danube. In the oaks and

willows, and on strips of land neighboring the marshes, flocks of herons, little egrets, black-crowned night herons, and spoonbills can also be found.

Around the marsh of the Evros of Turkey, in a vast pine forest, the golden eagle, the white-tailed eagle, the imperial eagle, and the European black vulture build their nests.

In other deltas of the Mediterranean, the lagoon area is next to a swampy coastland that is crossed by many channels. These waterways are sometimes blocked by reeds and waterlilies.

The water levels around these marshy areas rise and fall because of two factors: the seasonal change of temperature and the water level of the river flowing into the marsh. For instance, the water levels on the Guadalquivir and the Nile rivers vary a great deal throughout the seasons, but the level of the Danube River seldom rises or falls.

Seasons in the Marsh

In autumn, cranes and ducks leave the chilly north and seek out the marshy areas. During this season, the waters rise. Mammals take refuge on little hills that in winter become islands. Many prefer the rocky hills on Yugoslavia's Neretva delta where the Egyptian vulture makes its home. In February and March, when the geese and most of the ducks return to the north, coots, common moorhens, and mallards take their place and begin to nest.

In April, while the water level is sinking, breeding activity occurs everywhere in the marsh. In the midst of the reeds and the maquis, swarms of insects, mosquitoes, dipterans (flies) of every color, dragonflies, coleopterans (beetles), and butterflies appear. They become a plentiful food source for songbirds, such as reed warblers, great reed warblers, penduline tits, and bearded tits.

Among the plants live shrikes, perching birds with some of the characteristics and habits of birds of prey. One of them, the masked shrikes, can be observed from the Axios to the Ceyhan. Spotted woodpeckers and groups of Dalmatian pelicans can often be observed as well. The spotted woodpeckers live in the willow trees, while the Dalmatian pelicans stop to rest in the tall reeds of the winding Danube and Evros rivers. The Dalmatian pelicans and the eastern white pelicans have another favorite nesting place at the mouth of the Moraca River where it flows into Lake Scutari in Yugoslavia.

Across the sea in Greece, on the Mesta and the Axios,

Camargue, shown here, is an immense flood plain of 185,250 acres (75,000 ha) between the two arms of the Rhone Delta. The river's branches cause the Camargue's special marine and lagoon environment.

slender-billed gulls and Mediterranean gulls screech out high, shrill cries. Today, in the broad Veneta wetland areas, small groups of these two species can be found nesting.

The air, land surface, and underwater environments are all home to a variety of species. During their migrations, red-rumped swallows cross the sky above the Evros and the Danube rivers. On the marsh below, flocks of whiskered terns, gull-billed terns, collared pratincoles, and white wagtails hunt for their food.

Ducks, bitterns, and little bitterns, roam among the reeds in the low muddy waters of Hutovo Blato while seabirds strut along the shore. Nearby, huge laughing frogs (*Rana ridibiundfa*) croak. Some of the birds belong to the family Ardeidae, commonly known as herons, egrets, bitterns, and black-winged stilts.

Also in springtime, spoonbills, European flamingos, avocets, black-winged stilts, black-tailed godwit, curlews, dunlin, plovers, ruff, redshanks, and turnstones search deep in the marsh for food. They look for mollusks, shellfish, and small fish. High above, red kites, harriers, and marsh harriers wait for a chance to dive on their chosen prey. The white-tailed eagle, the lanner falcon, and the long-legged buzzard also live in the marshy lands of the Hutovo Blato.

Gulls, squacco herons, cattle egrets and little egrets, live in the drier grasslands near the marsh. To find food, they follow herds of oxen and horses and catch insects that are disturbed by the larger animals' hooves as they walk. Further east, on Egypt's Nile delta, the Egyptian goose and the spur-winged plover have finished nesting. Nearby, the greater sand plover and Kittlitz's plover are feeding.

Vultures and foxes find food in flatlands where shallow pools of water have evaporated. In clearings, great bustards (Old World game birds) search for grain, frogs, lizards, and field voles. Often, red deer or wild boar roam the marshy flats.

Autumn arrives again, bringing with it the rainy season. As the rain-swollen rivers flow down to the sea, new life reappears in the marshes. From the north, the ducks and geese fly down to their winter homes. Flocks of great crested grebes, scoters, teals, pintails, shovelers, tufted ducks, wigeons, mallards, garganeys, and shelducks return. Large species like the greylag goose, white-fronted goose, and red-breasted goose come down from Spain's Guadalquivir River to Egypt's Nile and the marshes of the Danube.

So it is that the delta's yearly cycle begins again. It seems as though the wildlife in the marshes could go on forever.

Opposite page, from right to left and top to bottom: Pictured are greater flamingos flying, gray herons nesting, bitterns trying to camouflage themselves among the canes, a spoonbill and little bittern looking for food in the shallow water, and a pelican on the bank. Drawn in characteristic behaviors, these are some of the many visitors to the wetlands of the Mediterranean.

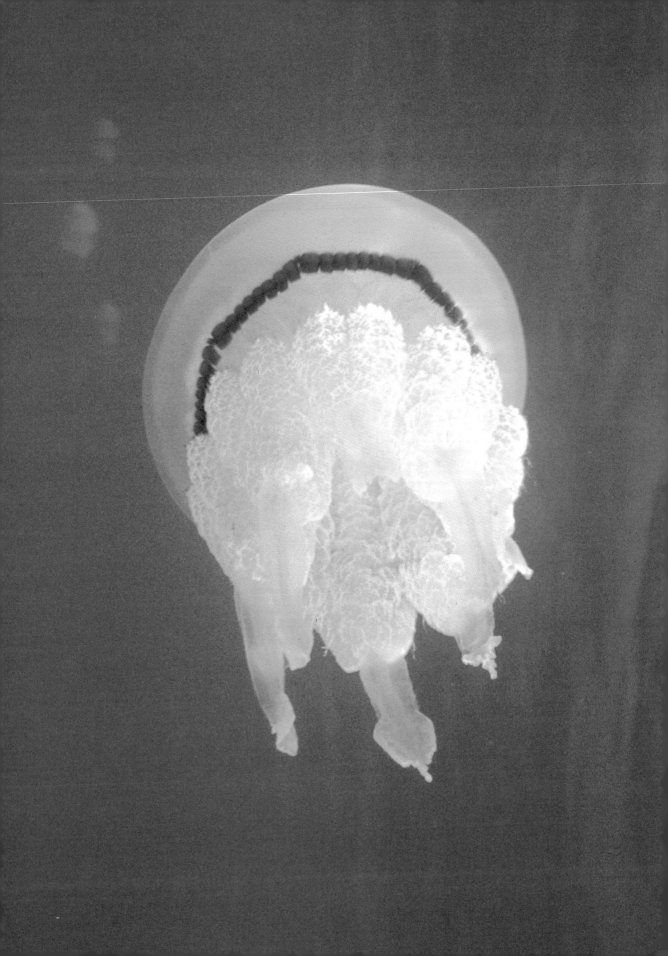

LIFE IN THE SEA

Geologists believe Europe and Africa were once united at Gibraltar and that the Mediterranean flowed into the Indian Ocean. Long ago, this link was cut off by the movement of continental shelves. The Mediterranean was divided into several huge lakes, sometimes connected by coastal rivers that carved deep into the floor of the sea.

Then, half a million years ago, sea life returned. Perhaps an earthquake or a rise in the level of the Atlantic Ocean caused a break at Gibraltar and a huge flood filled the basin. Today, taking an imaginary trip on the seabeds, it is possible to reconstruct this mythical landscape. The site of the major lakes could be retraced on the bottom of the ocean. In the underwater valleys and canyons, the course of the ancient rivers could be located.

The Abyssal Zones

There are three abyssal zones in the Mediterranean. An abyssal zone is an area so deep that it is impossible to measure or even touch the bottom. In the eastern, central, and western zones, the Mediterranean is deeper than 8,200 feet (2,500 m).

The western, or Herodotus zone, is 10,560 feet (3,219 m) deep. It is located between the southern coasts of Greece and Turkey north of Egypt. It is bounded on the west by the Strabo, Pliny, and Ptolemy trenches. This also marks the boundary of the African and European continental plateaus. To the north are the basins of Rhodes, Antalya, and Latakia. To the east is the steep slope of the Beirut escarpment. To the south is the fan-shaped slope of the Nile.

The central abyssal zone, named after the Ionian Sea, is located between Greece, Italy, and Lybia. It is as deep as 14,468 feet (4,410 m). Its northern boundary is the steep slope of the Calabrian rise that, with the valleys of Taranto and Otranto, reaches as far as the Adriatic basin. To the east is the Hellenic crest. On the south is the steep slope of the Sirte rise. To the west and northwest are the plateaus of Tunisia and Malta. In these areas, the sea is barely 886 feet (270 m) deep. From here, the zone continues across the channel of Sicily with a series of very low banks, including Birsa and Adventure, which range from 230 to 328 feet (70 to 100 m) deep.

The western abyssal zone, located between Sardinia and the Baleares, is 9,206 feet (2,806 m) deep. It is bounded on the east by the valley of the Egadi and by the canyon of Bizerte, which connects it to the Tyrrhenian basin. To the

Opposite page: The bluish rhizotome jellyfish is one of the best-known jellyfish. It can reach 23 inches (60 cm) in diameter and is common near the Mediterranean coasts, especially in spring.

Snakelocks anemone
(4 to 8 inches)

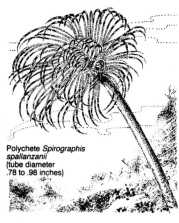

Polychete *Spirographis
spallanzanii*
(tube diameter
.78 to .98 inches)

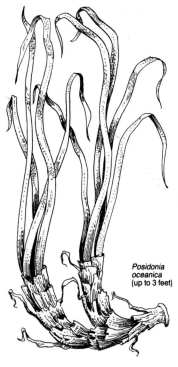

*Posidonia
oceanica*
(up to 3 feet)

northeast is the Corso-Ligurian basin and the steep slope, or scarp, and canyons of the Rhone fan. On the west, besides the Baleares, it is bounded by the scarp of the Ebro and by the Algerian basin that rises to connect to Gibraltar.

Light never reaches these seabeds since usually it can only penetrate down to 650 feet (200 m). In the Mediterranean however, it can sometimes reach down as far as 2,625 feet (800 m). Due to the lack of light, there are no green plants.

The Continental Shelf

Although most seabeds are between 820 and 13,100 feet (250 to 4,000 m) deep, the most sea life is found on the continental shelf. A continental shelf is still considered part of a continent, but it is an underwater extension of the land. Light can still penetrate, helping plants to grow abundantly. These underwater plants not only feed sea animals, but also provide shelter and hiding places for small fish, larvae, and eggs. The sun's rays and an abundance of mineral salts promote the development of phytoplankton, or plant plankton. Organisms of this group are very basic sea plants and form the beginning of the food chain of sea animals. Phytoplankton is eaten by zooplankton (animal plankton). These zooplankton are in turn eaten by invertebrates such as mollusks and crustaceans. Finally, the invertebrates are eaten by fish, birds, and mammals, including humans.

In the first 330 feet (100 m) are various animal associations, characteristic relationships formed by groups of animal species that live in the same area. They are named after the most common species. The associations vary according to the depth and the food available to the marine animals and plants.

On the muddy seabeds down to 330 feet (100 m) is the *Amphiura* community, which gets its name from a starfish genus having five long arms for creeping about. Living with them in harmony under the sea are the cnidarians of the genus *Pennatula*, the polychaetes *Terebella* and *Nephthysse* (marine worms), and the *Dentalium*, mollusks called "elephant's tusks." The shell of the mollusk is shaped like a tooth, and the mollusk lives stuck in the mud.

On sandy seabeds as deep as 160 feet (50 m) in the open sea is found the *Venus* community, named after a genus of mollusks with two shells. Other mollusks live in this community, too, including the well-known thin tellin, a mollusk in the genus *Tellina*.

Maia squinado
(body 5 to 6 inches)

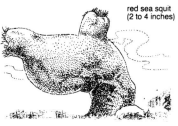

red sea squit
(2 to 4 inches)

purple sea urchin
(2 to 2.5 inches)

spiny
sea star
(1 to 2 inches)

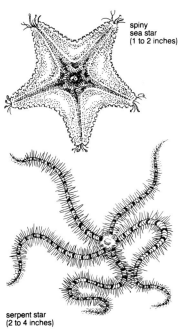

serpent star
(2 to 4 inches)

At the same depth, but favoring a muddy seabed near river mouths is the *Macoma* community. This community is made up mostly of *Macoma* and *Cardium,* two-shelled mollusks. One member of the genus *Macoma* is the common edible cockle, with little chambers inside its shell. Also found there are *Arenicola.* These marine worms, commonly called lugworms, are characterized by their stiff, short hairs or *setae.*

In shallow waters with sandy bottoms the community *Tellina* is found. It is dominated by mollusks and sea stars. Finally, in low, muddy waters, the *Syndesmya* community is found.

All kinds of crustaceans live in these communities, including European spiny lobsters, European lobsters, Norway lobsters, and Scyllaridae (slipper lobsters). They are also populated by large mollusks such as *Pinna nobilis,* the largest double-shelled sea animal in the Mediterranean. Its shell can be as large as 32 inches (80 cm).

A sandy and muddy coast forms where the sea doesn't drain completely, and the bed underneath is loose and sandy. Crawling animals adapt well here because they can bury themselves and hide by blending into the seabed. Among the fish to be found are the electric rays, fish with round, flat bodies, that hunt by sending out electric shocks. Another is the striped mullet that feeds on clusters of algae and the tiny animal communities living there.

The different beds of feeding material are loose, filled with nooks and crannies, and loaded with organic food. This is an ideal environment for microscopic species such as protozoans, rotifers, and turbellarians. These organisms are so tiny that they can be seen only through a microscope.

On the rocky coast, life in the sea has to adapt to the waves crashing against the rocky wall. In order to hang on and resist the force of the waves, many sea animals either have developed a sort of adhesive or suction-cup body part, or have evolved into an extremely flattened shape. The mollusk *Chiton* has the suction feature, as does the snakelocks anemone (an animal with flowerlike tentacles). Another mollusk, the *Patella,* is flat.

Other plants and animals cling together to protect each other from the crashing waves. For example, crabs and snakelocks anemone cling to one another. In other instances, a sea animal helps itself. For example, hermit crabs protect themselves by hiding in the cast-off shells of gastropods, mollusks with spiraled shells.

There are three different zones along the rocky coast. The first is above the tide line and is characterized by spray and salt. The second is the area between the high and low tide. The third is underneath the sea, ending where the light no longer reaches.

In the third zone there are common octopuses, sea urchins, date mussels, sea stars, red precious coral, and muricids—gastropods with spiny shells that give off a purple dye.

Small branches of red coral are typical of the Mediterranean in "bloom." The coral is not a plant and doesn't really bloom. In fact, coral is a colony of small snow white polyps whose limey shells create small branches. When the polyps move out of the coral cavities they hide in, they stretch out their tentacles and the branch seems to actually bloom. When the polyps are hiding, the branch looks "dry." The red color comes from the iron in the shells of the polyps.

Among the typical fish is the goby. Gobies are tiny fish with spiny fins that can change into suction cups. The goby will make any underwater hole a home, even a rusty tin can. Another typical fish, a species of porgy, is armed with a string of teeth enabling it to rip the limpets of the genus *Patella* from the rocks to which they cling.

Also found in this zone are the elegant needlefish and the sea horse. Large predators in the community are the moray and conger eels, with agile, snake-shaped bodies.

Some of the fish that populate the coastal waters of the Mediterranean are drawn. *From above to below, on this page:* Epinephelus guaza (a grouper), sea horse, red surmullet, *Dicenthrarcus labrax,* and *Solea vulgaris* (a sole). *Opposite page:* Chromis chromis (a damselfish), *Diplodus annularis* (a sargo), *Boops boops, Crenilabrus tinca,* and *Coris julis.*

The plants, fish, and invertebrates here are members of two groups. Benthic species live on the seabed and are grouped according to whether the bottom is sandy, muddy, or rocky. Pelagic species live in the open sea.

Among those living on the seabed are fish well adapted to life on the bottom of the sea. The common Atlantic sturgeon, a primitive fish slowly disappearing from the Mediterranean, is a good example. This sturgeon's sense of taste is not located in the tongue, but instead on the barbels, a "moustache" that grows on the front of the mouth.

Many fish adapt to the bottom of the sea by flattening and blending into the background. This is true of both fish with gristly tissue, or cartilage, like skates, electric rays, and sting rays, and those called "bony fish," such as sole, turbot, and plaice (flat, olive-brown fish with white spots).

The pelagic fish—those on the surface of the coastal waters or open sea—reproduce in great numbers. They gather in dense groups, or schools, of the same species. These schools are a way of saving energy and time. Swimming in the flow of other members of the school takes less energy than swimming alone.

The true sea travelers that have faithfully been visiting the Mediterranean for thousands of years are the European eel and the bluefin tuna. They reach the basin after a long migration. The larvae of the eel, born in the Sargasso Sea near North America, travel along the warm current of the gulf toward the Mediterranean basin until they reach the mouths of the rivers that empty into it. Their trip takes over two years. Finally the larvae, by now small, "blind" eels, swim up river. When they reach maturity, they return to breed in the Sargasso Sea.

Great schools of bluefin tuna invade the Mediterranean in April, after having wintered in the North Atlantic. The individuals reach sexual maturity at the age of three, when they weigh about 33 pounds (15 kg) and measure 3 feet (1 m) long. By age thirteen, they will weigh an average of 420 pounds (190 kg) and measure 9 feet (265 cm) long. These huge, metallic blue fish cut the surface of the Atlantic waters and enter the Strait of Gibraltar.

There are two main zones where they lay millions of eggs in May and June. One lies between the Iberian coast and the southern Baleares. The other, the most important, is in the triangle between Sardinia, Sicily, and Tunisia. Between July and September they migrate back to the North Sea.

SURVIVAL AND ECOLOGY

Since the time of the Phoenicians, Greeks, and Romans, the Mediterranean basin has changed greatly. The forests have been largely cut down, the coastal marshes have dried up, and the steppes, old and new, have been transformed into vast areas for the production of grain. None of the ancestors of the region would believe how much grain is now growing in what once was so dry.

Along with that, the density of the human population has increased dramatically. Many of the newly built cities and villages have been situated along the coast.

Effects of Habitat Destruction

Some bird species, such as sparrows, starlings, and larks, and carrion crows—which feed on dead flesh as vultures do—have not only adapted well to new situations, but they have also caused some changes in their own environment. Many other species have managed to lay claim to more and more space for their own ecological niches. Even though the surroundings may be considered artificial or only partly natural, these species have kept high populations.

On the other hand, species needing more special environments or certain foods have not survived well. Because their habitat has been changed, they have died off drastically. Especially hard-hit are the large animals, mammals, birds, and reptiles that need large areas with lots of food to survive.

In general, it is possible to reduce or reverse the effects of too much hunting or environmental change, unless it has become so great that it is permanent. Repopulating areas in which a species has become extinct is very hard to do, even if attempts are made to rebuild the habitat artificially. The species of animals that are most sensitive to any change in their environment are found in areas that are isolated from one another, or subdivided. They have few members, and never come in contact with one another.

This decline could be a problem without government protection, preservation of habitats, and changes in the way the land is used for agriculture. The needs of animals to feed off the land must be kept in mind. Following is a discussion of endangered species in the Mediterranean basin.

Mediterranean Monk Seal

"It rests inside its hollow caves, and falls asleep, and often around it sleep the seals, deformed race of beautiful Alosa, risen earlier from the waves, and the heavy fragrance

Opposite page: Behind the site of ancient Troy in the Turkish Province of Camukkale, one can see how recent agricultural techniques have discouraged the presence of wildlife throughout the basin.

Mediterranean monk seals swim in the Atlantic waters of Mauritania. The adult specimens can exceed 10 feet (3 m) in length and 771 pounds (350 kg) in weight. Very shy, these pinnipeds need peace and quiet, especially during the gestation period of eleven months and during the six to eight weeks the mother is nursing.

blown far from the deep sea." This is what Homer said about the Mediterranean monk sea in the *Odyssey*. This pinniped, which is an aquatic mammal whose limbs have been modified into flippers, has lived all over the world from the Greek poet's time until the last century. In recent times, however, it has been rapidly disappearing and is now almost extinct.

Its homes include Madiera, the Canary Islands, the western Sahara (region of Cap Blanc), the coasts of Mauritania, Morocco, Algeria, Lebanon and Turkey, the islands on the northern coast of Tunisia, some Greek and Yugoslavian islands, the Black Sea near Kaliakra, Sardinia, Sicily, and perhaps Israel. Sightings near Sardinia and Sicily are unofficial. Outside the Mediterranean region, the monk seals are only found above and below the equator where the winters hover around 68°F (20°C), the same temperature as the sea. There are no more than five hundred monk seals in the whole area.

The monk seal is extremely wary of humans and is thus hard to observe. Only people fishing have occasion to see them. The monk seal, like all the pinnipeds, feeds on fish, and sometimes chews holes in fishing nets to get an easy meal.

But the biggest enemy of the monk seal may be the sport motorboats of tourists, especially those who are attracted to the area by development along the coasts. Seals by nature do not avoid sunlight. But they must take refuge in underwater grottos to be completely safe from people. The seals retire to these underwater caves to give birth and to raise their young. Unlike their ancestors, many newborn pups never get to see the light of day. They often end up not getting enough vitamin D, because the sun's rays are needed to activate the production of vitamin D in their bodies. This deficiency causes rickets, a dangerous softening of the bones. The monk seal could disappear from the Mediterranean any day now, unless its sea coast habitat is protected.

White-Headed Duck

The white-headed duck is without a doubt one of the rarest members of the European anatids, or duck and goose family. Lately it has been disappearing from Italy, Corsica, and Greece. The largest population of white-headed ducks today lives in Spain. In 1960, it was estimated that a total of fifty pairs lived in the whole country. In 1972 the population

was forty to one hundred ducks. In 1982, zoologists counted seventy-four adults and nineteen chicks.

Because the white-headed duck population in Spain is threatened with extinction, the Spanish people have set up a small association called *Amigos de la Malvasia* (which means "Friends of the White-Headed Duck"). It acts as a lifeguard for the species, trying to protect them in every way: from controls and regulations, censuses and studies, to broadcasts that make the public more aware of the danger of the ducks' extinction. A main goal of the *Amigos de la Malvasia* is to remove pollution from the wetlands often visited by white-headed ducks.

Other efforts to protect this species, paid for by the European Economic Community (EEC), are in progress in Sardinia. The goal is to repopulate the ponds where white-headed ducks stopped reproducing regularly in the 1970s. The future seems brighter for this bird in North Africa and Kazakhstan (east of the Caspian Sea), but the entire world population is estimated at only fifteen thousand.

Purple Gallinule

The purple gallinule is a breathtaking, sky blue member of the Rallidae (waging bird) family. It looks like a crane and was originally spread through the marshy regions of Spain, Italy, Greece, Morocco, Algeria, and Tunisia. Similar to a large moorhen, it has a narrow body that is handy for squeezing between canes and tall grasses. The purple gallinule moves its feet slowly and gracefully, as if riding a bicycle in slow motion. Like a peacock, it often raises its short tail to show off its snow-white tail feathers. It feeds on grain, plant roots, mollusks, and insects, grasping its favorite plant food with its claws.

The purple gallinule has now completely disappeared from the Italian peninsula, Sicily, Greece, and the Balearic Islands. The last European homes of the species remain in Sardinia and the mouth of the Guadalquivir River in Spain. There, about one hundred pairs will hopefully produce offspring to increase the population.

Much can be learned from the history of the purple gallinule in Sicily. In 1929, observers noted that 1,500 of the birds were being killed off each year in the ponds of Lentini. By 1931, the number killed annually dropped to one hundred. Fourteen years later, the bird still nested in Sicily, but only rarely. Finally, in 1969, experts indicated that draining the ponds and marshes, which were the bird's

During the day the purple gallinule almost always stays in the thickness of the canebrakes. If it crosses an open lagoon it does so in a great hurry. Around dawn or sunset it can be seen out in the open, sometimes taking flight *(opposite page)*. One can get fairly close to observe it.

refuge in Sicily and Sardinia, was causing the bird to disappear.

Nothing could have been more true. After the draining of Lake Lentini in 1951, the purple gallinule disappeared from the largest island of the Mediterranean. In contrast, in some wetlands that received special protection in Sardinia, the purple gallinule has not only survived but is thriving and reproducing.

Sea Turtle

Among living reptiles, the sea turtle is the most threatened with extinction. They are members of the family Chelonid and are characterized by being enclosed in a double shell. The Mediterranean is probably not their most

The phases of nesting of the loggerhead sea turtle are pictured, from the time the female approaches the beach where she will deposit the eggs to the moment that the hatchlings run to the sea.

important breeding ground. Here the common loggerhead reproduces regularly. Four other species appear in the basin: the leatherback, the green turtle, the Atlantic ridly, and the olive ridly. The last two turtles are rarely found.

The sea turtle spends its entire life in the sea, feeding mostly on algae and marine plants, but also on mollusks, crustaceans, and fish. It comes on land only to lay its eggs. Leading a solitary life, the sea turtle will form small groups in the mating season. The sea turtle actually migrates with an "internal compass," finding its way by the position of the sun and stars.

Reproduction takes place every two years. The eggs the female lays may have been fertilized up to a year earlier. Nesting occurs at night. The female crawls about 160 to 200 feet (50 to 60 m) from the shoreline. Then she digs in the sand with her back flippers, forming a big wide hole where she deposits as many as two hundred eggs an hour. Then the female covers the hole and returns to the sea.

The eggs are incubated by the sun for about two months. Then the tiny newborn, about 2 inches (5 cm) long, quickly heads for the sea. This is one of the most dangerous moments in a sea turtle's life. All kinds of predators—mammals, seabirds and fish—wait to attack for the young turtles, and many don't make it from the nest to the sea.

In order to survive, the sea turtles must have safe places on the beaches for laying their eggs. But these beaches have been taken over by humans all over the Mediterranean, especially in the last thirty years. They have been changed to make room for tourists. Towns and swimming facilities have been built. Sport motorboat traffic has increased and poses a big threat to the sea turtle. Its life is further complicated by illegal capturing or netting by people fishing. Between 1940 and 1970, about 25,000 turtles were killed in the Mediterranean alone. There is reason to feel nervous about the future of the sea turtle.

GUIDE TO AREAS OF NATURAL INTEREST

The Mediterranean region, just like other natural regions of the world, looks very different today from the way it looked in the past. The very word *Mediterranean* gives people the idea of a warm, blue sea, villages with white houses, sun, hot summers, and so on. But to experts, the same word *Mediterranean* means a large valley covered with mastic trees and oleander, the chattering of a Sardinian warbler, or the joyous sound of the trills and warbling of a serin. When one thinks of the Mediterranean from a biological and geographical point of view, it is a combination of different ecosystems. To really get the whole picture of the Mediterranean, one would have to visit all its corners: the Uccellina maquis, the banks of Camargue, a deserted beach in Algeria.

The most unspoiled environments facing the Mediterranean have very little protection today. Many of them are probably in danger and could lose much of their size and appeal. To try to put together a "complete catalog" of these environments would not only be a huge amount of work, but also a waste of time because the descriptions of how they looked would be constantly changing.

For example, sand dunes can disappear, along with all their characteristic vegetation, as happened at the Doñana Reserve. Coastal lakes can be drained, such as Lake Lentini in Sicily and Lake Amik in Turkey, causing rare birds to disappear. Vast expanses of maquis can be burned to the ground and plowed under to build houses and towns for tourism. Some of this is happening all over the Mediterranean.

What can be done about it? Certainly, governments can get involved to stop drastic changes in natural areas. There are associations to join that are concerned with nature conservation. The members support local plans to build new parks and reserves and promote conservation and wise use of natural resources. In addition, it would be invaluable to keep in mind a list of precious, beautiful areas still in their natural state and to then pay special attention to protecting them. In this chapter are names and descriptions of these areas: national parks, regional parks, and nature reserves.

This is not by any means a complete or exclusive list of these areas. Instead, the list includes a good variety of areas that are easiest to visit. A small nature reserve located in a peaceful country that is well provided with trails and tourist information centers is generally more interesting than a bigger but remote area in a country difficult to visit.

Opposite page: An explanatory poster is studied at the entrance of the Samaria Gorge, a natural reserve on the island of Crete.

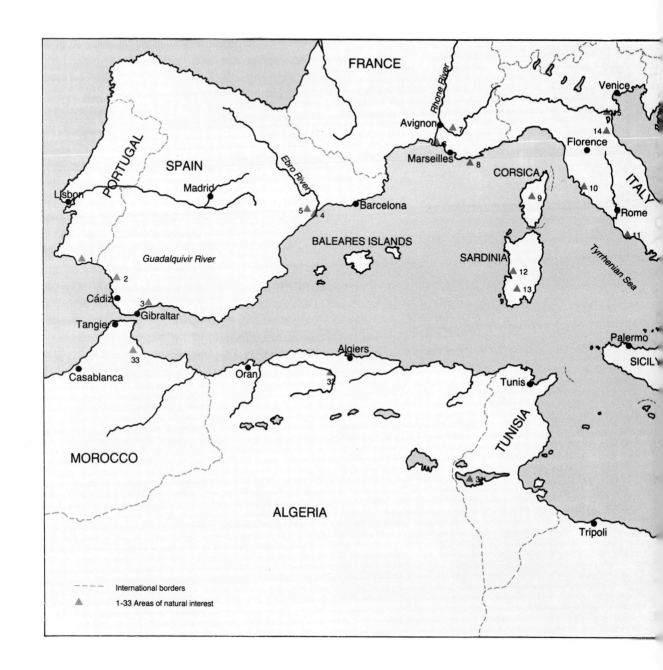

Map legend:
- - - - - International borders
▲ 1-33 Areas of natural interest

PORTUGAL

Ria Formosa (1)

A map of interesting nature areas, chosen because of their protection, the flora and fauna, and accessibility is pictured.

This natural reserve stretches 65 miles (105 km) along the Algarve coasts south of Faro and Tavira. It is a marshy-lagoon complex, with tourist areas and salt basins. At times, it has the look of flowery Mediterranean vegetation. Herons, bitterns, shorebirds, and ducks winter there. In addition, visitors encounter European flamingos, spoonbills, white storks, black-winged stilts, gull-billed terns, purple gallinules, and pin-tailed sand grouse.

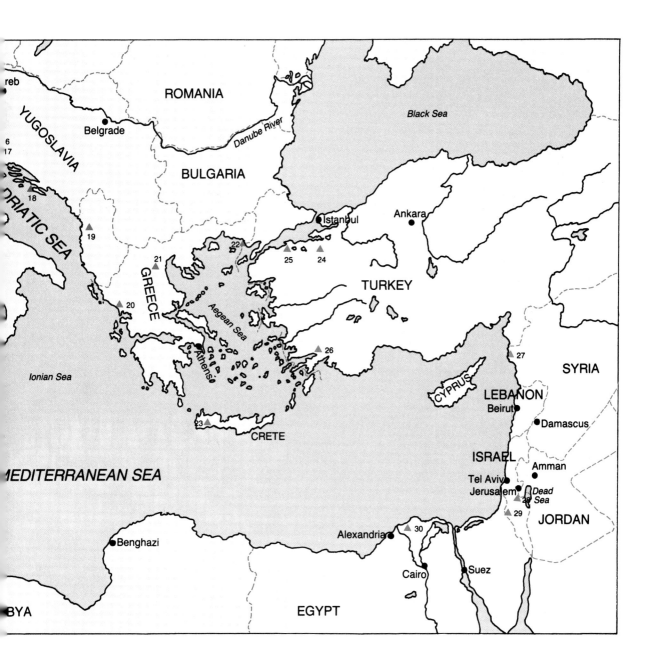

SPAIN

Doñana (2)

The Doñana National Park spans 465 miles (750 km) on the Guadalquivir delta north of Cadiz. It can be reached from Jerez de la Frontera, from Seville, or from Huelva. However, permission must be obtained in advance by contacting the Doñana Biological Station, c/o Paraguay 1, Sevilla. Although Doñana has its own nature trails and observatories, visitors must hire a local guide to be shown around. It is an area full of dunes and coastal marshes, separated by cork oak maquis. It has been a royal hunting reserve for centuries, and has been preserved unchanged to this day.

The vegetation most often seen is erica and stone pine on the sand dunes, and glasswort and mock lemo in the marshes. The common brake grows in the more arid zones. There are great colonies of herons and bitterns. Other species of nesting birds found are imperial eagles, greater flamingos, white-headed ducks, reddish brown ruddy shelducks, marbled teal, purple gallinules, pin-tailed sand grouse, and stone curlews. It is also an important winter home for geese and ducks. Other noteworthy animals are Eurasian river otters, ichneumons, genets, European wildcats, spotted lynx, red deer, and fallow deer.

Serrania de Ronda (3)

The 136-mile (220 km) Serrania de Ronda national reserve is a lime-filled massif, the center part of a mountain ridge, west of Malaga. It is reached most easily from Ronda or from Cain. There are no prepared trails. Below 4,921 feet (1,500 m), one crosses a classic garique, left over from ancient forests of holm oak and oak. Around 5,905 feet (1,800 m) is a typically ruined forest of maple and oak, called the "quejigal" in Spanish. At times, Spanish fir trees are seen, as is the winged iris in spring. The Pyrenean ibex and three eagles—the golden eagle, booted eagle, and Bonelli's eagle are the most common local animals. Griffon vultures and other big predators are also very common.

Ebro delta (4)

Only six of the 397 miles (640 km) of the delta are protected. A national hunting reserve takes up almost 1 mile (1.6 km). The rest is cultivated for rice or used as salt springs. Ebro delta can be reached from Amposta and can be crossed easily by car.

It is a wetland composed of dunes and salty lagoons. Many interesting birds from all over the world winter there: shorebirds, gulls, common terns, greater flamingos and ducks, among which are the pochard, shoveler, and wigeon.

Tortosa y Beceite (5)

There is a national reserve 182 miles (293 km) long, a couple of miles west of Tortosa (where the access road ends) and the Ebro delta. Closed during hunting season, it is a series of alternating peaks and valleys with guided trails. The highest peak is Mount Caro at 4,747 feet (1,447 m). *Quercus coccifera* (berry-producing oak trees) and Portuguese oak are mixed in with Austrian pine and Aleppo pine.

Visitors also see beautiful beech wood and robust English yew tasso. *Genista scorpius* is one of the most representative spiny shrubs. Black vultures, goshawks, sparrow hawks, golden eagles, and eagle owls are among the birds found there. Pyrenean ibex, genets, European wildcats, and mouflon also roam this area nestled between Mediterranean and Alpine surroundings.

FRANCE

Camargue (6)

A regional park 590 miles (950 km) long at the mouth of the Rhone River, the Camargue contains two branches of the Petit and Grand Rhone and spreads outside the Grand Rhone up to the Malegal pond. Two routes take visitors there: from Arles, north of the park; and on the sea from the opposite side right on Camargue Island. There tourists would depart from Les Saintes-Marie-de-la-Mer, which was a gathering place of wandering European gypsies. The park has several bird observatories and a biology station at Tour du Valat. At Gines there is a main information center and an ornithological "park" full of birds.

The park is divided into three reserves. The main one is Vaccares pond, a national reserve. The other two are much smaller: the Imperial reserve on the pond of the same name, managed by the government of Les Saintes-Maries, and the private reserve of Tour du Valat, managed by the biology station of the same name near Le Sambuc.

These park environments are a combination not likely to be seen elsewhere. Visitors encounter dunes, salty lagoons, salty steppes, coastal forests, rice paddies, grapevines, and corn. The vegetation runs from stone pine and the maquis of the dunes to sea lavender and phillyred of the salty steppe, to the canebrakes of the ponds, to willows, European alder, and poplars of the coastal forest. Nesting bird life is rich in many species: herons and bitterns, shorebirds, and gulls, not to mention the famous European flamingos, that have the best-thriving European colonies here. Continuing the list, there are marsh harriers, harriers, bee-eaters, rollers, hoopoe, great spotted cuckoos, and many, many songbirds. Among the mammals found are wild rabbits, beavers, coypu, common weasels, and the famous Camargue black oxen and white horses of Camargue that graze freely on the salty steppe.

Lubéron (7)

Lubéron is a regional nature park, 746 miles (1,200 km) long, east of Avignon. It can also be reached via Aix-en-

Provence. Lubéron doesn't have prepared trails, but it does have a good information center. It is a lime-filled range, and its highest elevation of 3,691 feet (1,125) is called Lubéron Peak, located north of the river Durance. It is fairly cultivated on the lowest slopes, and rich in archaeological sites. The broad prairies of lavender color the country blue in the summertime. The oak is the dominant tree, except for 6 miles (10 km) of Atlantic cedar near Bonnieux. The slope that faces the Durance is covered with thick, shrubby Mediterranean maquis. The typical inhabitant of this zone is the Sardinian warbler.

Port Cros (8)

The national park of Port Cros, in the Gulf of Hyeres, extends to the islet of the same name and the corresponding continental plateau. Visitors travel there by ferry from Le Lavandou, a small port east of Tolone. The entire nature reserve is open all year, with the exception of the small island of Bagaud, an intact nature reserve.

In the park there is a Mediterranean forest in its original state. There are holm oak and Aleppo pines scattered among typical plants of the maquis: wild olive, myrtle, strawberry trees, mastic trees, cistuses, and erica.

There are also some very interesting small animals. These include European leaf-fingered geckos, painted frogs, ladder snakes, and Montpellier snakes. Among the birds are Cory's shearwaters, big-billed puffins, peregrine falcons, blue rock thrushes, hoopoes, bee-eaters, scops owls, and herring gulls. Among the mammals are wild rabbits.

The variety of insects is also worth mentioning. There are two hundred different species of butterflies, such as the *Charaxes jasius* which feeds on the strawberry tree. There are six hundred different species of beetles. The seabeds of the park are among the few protected seabeds of Europe and lie up to 1,968 feet (600 m) off the coast.

Corsica (9)

Corsica is a national regional park of 579 sq. miles (1,500 sq. km) that surrounds a mountain range often higher than 6,561 feet (2,000 m). The park also extends into the west toward Porto. Access to the park is from Ajaccio, Corte, and Porto. With special permission, usually given just to researchers, one can get to the nature reserve of Scandola along the north coast of the Gulf of Porto. Marked trails, stocked shelters, summer horseback excursions, and skiing in winter are the possibilities available to the naturalist who wants to get around the park in an "ecological" way.

Visitors can see fifty-eight species of plants native to the area. Some of the best are the Corsican pine and the blooming crocus and *Romulea*. There are plants one would expect to find in a Mediterranean region, such as cork oaks and strawberry trees. Thanks to the many different environments here, visitors find birds such as lammergiers, ospreys, marsh harriers, goshawks, Alpine accentors, red-breasted nuthatches, Marmora's warblers, Audouin's gulls, Cory's shearwaters, and purple herons. On the beautiful rocks of Scandola, nests the golden eagle along with species already mentioned. Among the mammals to be seen are the mouflon, and in the maquis, the dark green racer, the only ground snake in Corsica.

ITALY

Maremma Toscana (10)

Maremma Toscana is a regional nature park south of Grosseto. Access is from Albarese (where the information center is located) with guided tours on the nature paths.

Limey cliffs are covered with thick Mediterranean maquis with holm trees, strawberry trees, turkey oaks, hornbeams, myrtles, ericas and scattered dwarf fan palm. Bays and caves are found where the rock leans over into the sea. These areas are of much interest to paleontologists, who study history through plant and animal fossils.

On the other side of the Ombrone, extend the saltwater marshes of Trappola, where one can find wild horses and Maremma oxen. Permanent residents are wild boar, crested porcupines, badgers, European wildcats, skunks, and fallow deer. Here reproduce short-toed eagles, hobbies, peregrine falcons, black-winged stilts, kingfishers, oystercatchers and bee-eaters. Also present are migratory birds like ospreys and white storks.

Circeo (11)

The Circeo National Park, which extends for 32 sq. miles (84 sq. km), begins slightly north of Terracina in four distinct areas: the promontory, or projecting rocks, the coastal dunes and lakes, the woods (in a genuine swamp area), and Zannone Island.

Besides the flora one would expect to see here, there are also dwarf fan palms in the limey massif of the promontory, sea daffodils, Phoenician juniper and plum juniper, two species of juniper trees that produce cones and berries. In the woods are many interesting trees—Hungarian oak, English oak, and European ash—in addition to many species of mushrooms. On the island are lavender, ragworts, and centauries. Many birds make this their winter home, such as herons and bitterns, shorebirds, ducks, divers, European flamingos, blackwinged stilts, marsh harriers, short-eared owls, and ospreys. Among the mammals other than the commonly seen wild boar are wild rabbits, crested porcupines, pine martens, and the introduced Egyptian mongooses.

The park is fascinating to archaeologists, with its Greek, Roman, and Medieval structures. Paleontologists value it because of the caves named Guattari, Fossellone, and Caterattino.

Sale Porcus (12)
Giara di Gesturi (13)

Located among the Oristano ponds, Sale Porcus is a saltwater marsh that constitutes a natural reserve rich in bird species. It is famous because it attracts thousands of wintering European flamingos. In addition, it is host to other rare forms, such as white-headed ducks, shelducks, and purple gallinules, as well as cormorants, grebes, herons, and bitterns.

East of Oristano, near the complex of ancient stone towers in Sardinia called "Barumini," rises the high salty plain of Giara di Gesturi. This plain extends for 17 sq. miles (45 sq. km) and is covered in cork oak mixed with strawberry trees, myrtles, and mastic trees, and scattered throughout with ponds. It has about three hundred wild horses, which are as small as ponies but much more agile and graceful.

Punte Alberete (14)
Bosco della Mesola (15)

The oasis of Punte Alberete and the Mesola wood, comprising the entire natural reserve of Bassa dei Frassini-Balanzette, are two of the most beautiful wetlands of the territory Valli di Comacchio-Po delta.

The oasis of Punte Alberete, which covers 1 sq. mile (3 sq. km) can be reached from Ravenna. It offers guided visits, and is also equipped with observatories. The marsh area is divided in half by the Lamonte River. It is made of bogs, coastal lagoons, and flooded forests of willows and poplars. The rare water parsnip grows there.

On the east side, the area is surrounded by the coastal pine forest of S. Vitale. It offers an ideal environment for nesting egrets, night herons, squacco herons, and grey herons. Nesting there are also glossy ibis, mallards, ferrugineous ducks, garganey and shovelers. The Mesola wood, accessible from Volano and Pomposa, is characterized by holm oak, mixed in the wetlands with white poplars, pines, European ash, and English oak. Deer, fallow deer, and wild boars are among the many fauna to be found.

YUGOSLAVIA

Paklenica (16)

This national park in the Velebit Mountains is located a little north of Zadar. It can be reached from Starigrad-Paklenica. Guided trails and an information center are being prepared. It is a complex of rough limestone gorges rising 1,312 feet (400 m) at some points. It is founded on two main canyons, Mala Kapela and Velika Kapela. There are numerous caves: the most important are those called Manita Pec and Jama Vodarica. The highest peak, Vaganjski, rises to 5,768 feet (1,758 m). Beech and Austrian pine cover the highest slopes of the valleys below the barren peaks. Where the Mediterranean influence becomes more noticeable, there are pubescent oak, European ash and dwarf junipers with a thick underbrush. Species native only to this area can also be observed, such as *Saxifraga velebitica* and *Campanula velebitica*. The kinds of fauna that live here are an indication of the inaccessibility of the area. Birds include griffon vultures, short-toed eagles, eagle owls, golden eagles, black woodpeckers, three-toed woodpeckers, and nutcrackers. Mammals include brown bears, roe deer, martens and European wildcats. Also interesting are the reptiles and amphibians, especially the salamanders and sand snakes.

Worth mentioning as a source of fossils is the canyon of Obrovac along the route of the Zrmanja, 15 miles (25 km) south.

Krka (17)

The Krka Nature Reserve covers 54 sq. miles (140 sq km) and lies along the Krka River, near Sibenik. It can be reached inexpensively by bus.

The reserve is a complex of waterfalls. The Skradinski is 1,640 feet (500 m) wide with a cascade falling 164 feet (50 m). There are seventeen falls in all, and they are constantly changing because the water leaves its own limestone deposits called "travertine." The complex also include lakes where the valley widens. At 3 sq. miles (9 sq. km), Visovacko is the largest.

North of that is a hard-to-reach rocky section, and further up are woods of Aleppo pine, Manna ash, and oriental hornbeams. Above that woods, holm oak maquis are found to the south, on lower slopes which are not so steep.

Among the fauna, the trout *Salmo obtusirostris* is a native of the area. Its typical birdlife includes Sardinian warblers, sombre tits, booted eagles, and Egyptian vultures. Among the mammals one can see are martens, skunks, and Eurasian river otters.

Following pages: One of the waterfalls that agitate the course of the Yugoslavian river Krka, along which a guided nature reserve has been set up is pictured.

Mljet (18)

Mljet is a national park of 12 sq. miles (31 sq. km), located on an island with the same name. Visitors can get to the south entrance by boat from Dubrovnik, and to the north from Zuljana on the peninsula of Pelješac. Two salt lakes, Mali Jezero and Veleki Jezero are connected with a channel to the sea, and are typical of this area. The park also has hotels and camping grounds.

Of great interest is the forest of Aleppo pine and holm oak with clusters of strawberry trees, heath, myrtle, mastic trees, plum juniper, Phoenician juniper, and common juniper, in addition to carob trees and laurel.

The ichneumon fly was brought to the region. It lives as a parasite in the eggs of other insects and reptiles, and has practically destroyed Mljet's reptiles and amphibians. Surviving, however, are the slender racer, the *Lacerta oxycephala* and the Turkish gecko.

ALBANIA

Dajtit (19)

Dajtit is a national park extending 11 sq. miles (30 sq. km) northeast of Tirana. It is a peak 5,288 feet (1,612 m) high, covered by a virgin forest of Bosnian pines, Austrian pine, silver fir, and European beech. On the side that faces the Ionian Sea, Aleppo pine and holm oak mix on the lower slopes. The most common species found are golden eagles, booted eagles and perhaps Bonelli's eagles, griffon vultures, lesser kestrels, peregrine falcons, black woodpeckers, brown bears, gray wolves and spotted lynx.

GREECE

Arta (20)

The oasis of the Gulf of Arta contains 69 sq. miles (180 sq. km) of wetlands of international importance. One can reach it via the city of the same name, or from Prveza. The marsh area, created from the Louros and Arachthos deltas, added to the sandy coastline of Salaora and is connected to the Ionian by the Straits of Aktion. Canebrakes and glassworts are the dominant species of vegetation. Fauna are the spur-tailed Mediterranean tortoise in rare tracts of maquis, and striped mullet in the lagoon waters. Birds include Dalmatian and white pelicans, pygmy cormorants, purple herons, glossy ibis, little egrets, squacco herons, white storks, black-winged stilts, avocets, gull-billed terns, collared pratincoles, and bee-eaters.

Olympus (21)

The massif, with the peaks of Olympus at 9,570 feet (2,917 m), Pagos at 8,799 feet (2,682 m), and Livadhaki at 7,762 feet (2,366 m), and the high basin of Mavrolongos, make up this national park of 15 sq. miles (40 sq. km).

On the northeast slope, there is not much sun. The vegetation between 2,500 and 3,200 feet (800 and 1,000 m) is made up of Greek maquis Judas trees, *Pistacia terebinthus* (pistachio nut trees that yield turpentine, mastic trees, European beech, Austrian pine, and Balkan pine. There are also other species native only to either the massif or the Balkan Peninsula: *Campanula oreadum* (mountain plants bearing bell-shaped flowers), *Viola striisnotata* (flowers like violets or pansies that cover the ground), *Jankaea heldreichii,* and *Saxifraga spruneri.*

The most characteristic fauna of the area includes brown bears, jackals, and gray wolves. Among the birds are sparrow hawks, golden eagles, black vultures, green woodpeckers, Alpine accentors, ortolan buntings, and rock buntings.

Maritsa (22)

The Maritsa delta, 108 sq. miles (280 sq. km) between the Greek and Turkish banks is partially protected but only on the Greek side. Because it is a military zone, there is a certain amount of protection already provided.

The marsh complex is mainly in Greek territory. Together with Gala Lake in Turkey, it is surrounded by enormous forests of Austrian pine.

Four species of terns (including the only colony of sandwich terns in Greece), spur-winged plovers, avocets, black-winged stilts, collared pranticoles, redshanks, Dalmatian pelicans, black storks, glossy ibis, golden eagles, imperial eagles, booted eagles, white-tailed eagles, European black vultures, white-backed woodpeckers, Syrian woodpecker, and especially many other wintering birds (ducks and geese), represent the abundant bird life. Among the reptiles are the turtles: spur-tailed Mediterranean tortoises, European tortoises, European pond turtles, and *Mauremys caspica.*

Orymos (23)

This national park of 19 sq. miles (49 sq. km) is found on the island of Crete south of Hania. It is structured on a series of parallel gorges that cut the Lefka Ori ("white mountains") from north to south. Visitors may enter overland from Hania from the Kiloskala refuge. A marked trail 10 miles (16 km) long with a slope of 4,265 feet (1,300 m) crosses the main gorge, Samaria, a nature reserve of 3 sq. miles (8 sq. km). From there, it drops off into the sea at Aghia Roumeli.

Samaria Gorge is bordered by walls of red rock 1,000 to 2,000 feet (300 to 600 m) high, and is 10 to 16 feet (3 to 5 m) wide at the narrowest point. Ravens, choughs, jackdaws, golden eagles, griffons, Egyptian vultures, lammergeiers, and chukar are the most characteristic bird species. Very visible are the Cretean wild goats, whose population is thriving. Other park mammals include stone martens, badgers, and common weasels.

TURKEY

Ulu Dağ (24)
Kuscenneti (25)

Ulu Dağ is a national park of 378 sq. miles (980 sq. km). It is southeast of Bursa where entry is by car or cable car. It has skiing facilities and marked trails. The mountain, which is 8,343 feet (2,543 m) high, was known in ancient times as Olympus. It has slopes covered with a typical holm oak maquis, which changes gradually to Aleppo pine further up. Birds include Levant sparrow hawks, lesser-spotted eagles, lesser kestrels, chukars, black partridges, ring ouzels, somber tits, rufous chats, and crossbills.

Approximately 62 miles (100 km) from Bursa near Kuscenneti there is a lake called Lake Kus. *Kus* means "of the birds." (It was actually called "Manyas," until a few years ago when someone had the good idea to rename it after its inhabitants.) One can also spot Dalmatian pelicans, cormorants, spoonbills, glossy ibis, night herons, and Cetti's warblers.

Koycegiz (26)

A salt lake of 37 sq. miles (96 sq. km) flows into the sea near a narrow natural canal south of the city of Koycegiz, 38 miles (62 km) from Marmaris. This area, together with the mountain chain that overlooks it, is a hunting reserve.

Small marsh areas surround this lake that receives water from numerous thermal springs. Mixed in are banana plantations and palm groves. North of Koycegiz are found Mediterranean flora such as carob trees, myrtle, oleander and pistachio, and Alpine flora, such as Aleppo pine and Lebanon cedar.

Little bitterns, purple herons, little egrets, ruddy shelducks, Rüppell's warblers, collared doves, and laughing doves are the birds to observe on the lake. One can even get a glimpse of the golden eagle and Bonelli's eagle. In the mountains are gray wolves, jackals, leopards, fallow deer, and wild goats.

SYRIA

Jebel el Ansariya (27)

This forest reserve, which covers 58 sq. miles (150 sq. km), is east of Latakia. It is the most beautiful of the few

wooded areas still remaining in Syria. The Jebel is a chain of mountains with a maximum height of 5,125 feet (1,562 m). It runs parallel to the coast for more than 25 miles (40 km), and is bounded on the east by the last spurs of the Great Rift, into which the Orontes River flows.

Ground-level vegetation is Mediterranean, with Aleppo pine, kermes oak, valonia oak, pistachio, myrtle, laurel, and spiny calycotome. Then, at about 1,000 feet (305 m), it becomes woods of European beech, European alder, and pine. The fauna icludes typically Eurasian species such as roe deer, bears, fallow deer and badgers. Striped hyenas, jackals, spotted lynx, antelope, and gazelles are of Indo-african origin. Lammergeiers, Egyptian vultures, Bonelli's eagles, spur-winged plovers, cream-colored coursers, Audouin's gulls, great spotted cuckoos, little swifts, woodpeckers, and red-rumped swallows are the birds that are met from the coast to the river.

ISRAEL

En Gedi (28)

En Gedi is a natural reserve of 69 sq. miles (180 sq. km) reached by car or bus from Beersheba or Jerusalem. A waterfall with two cascades, a small lake, and springs make the En Gedi oasis in the Dead Sea region a pleasant place.

The vegetation consists of palm groves, Euphrates poplar, tamarisk, ferns, and canebrakes. The fauna—except for a few reptiles, the striped hyenas that dwell around the border of the oasis, and the hyrax—essentially consists of birds such as black-headed bulbuls, Tristam's starlings, house sparrows, blackcaps, olivaceous warblers, white-crowned black wheatears, shore larks, laughing doves, and long-legged buzzards. Crabs have been seen in the waters of the small lake.

En Avdat (29)

This park of 1.5 sq. miles (4 sq. km) is south of Beersheba in the Negev Desert. It includes the ancient Nabatean-Byzantine city of Avdat, a canyon with two ponds, and one spring.

Spiny acacia and pistachio nut trees of the Atlas are the two tree forms that can be found in the desert on the rim of the canyon. Willow and Euphrates poplar grow at the bottom. Iris and Nege crocus bloom all year long, as do other flowers. Monitor lizards, *Agama stellio*, and Palestine vipers are the reptile species that are most easily seen. Much harder to spot are the mammals, mostly nocturnal, such as gerbils, Rüppell's foxes, and caracals. Also counted among them are Nubian ibexes and hyraxes.

Bird life includes griffon vultures, long-legged buzzards, desert wheatears, white-crowned black wheatears, crested larks, and short-toed larks. Further south, the crater of Machtesh Ramon is loaded with fossils, such as one of the Tanystropheus (a giant lizard with a giraffelike neck). Descending to Eilat, there is an underwater nature reserve of corals with an underwater observatory and aquarium. From there one can reach the biblical park of Hai Bar near the Yotvata oasis. The park contains Nubian ibexes, antelope, gazelles, ostriches, fallow deer, wild goats, and oryx, in a forest of acacia. King Solomon's Mines are located further on in Timna.

EGYPT

Burullus (30)

Burullus is a lagoon in practically its natural state on the Nile Delta. It can be reached on the west from Burg Migheizil, a town in front of the home of the famous Rosetta stone—a tablet that provided a key to deciphering ancient Egyptian writing.

The lagoon area is surrounded, especially near El Haddadi, by citrus groves, corn fields, and date palm plantations. On the dunes are sea daffodils, African valerians, and Thymelaea. In the marshes are lotuses and, very rarely, papyri. The rich local bird life includes Egyptian geese, little egrets, night herons, little bitterns, hoopoes, laughing doves, common bulbuls, belted kingfishers, Egyptian vultures, black kites, cream-colored coursers, yellow wagtails and meadow pipits. Among the mammals are gerbils, Rüppelli's foxes, and fennecs.

TUNISIA

El Djerid (31)

Chott el Djerid covers about 3,500 sq. miles (9,000 sq. km). This salt-lake desert west of Djerba and Gabes can be reached via Kemali. Another point of departure is Tozeur. This expanse of salt flats stretches east to Chott el Fedjadj and west to Chott Melghir (in Algeria). To the north is the steppe along the slopes of the Djebel el Asker; to the south is the desert of the southern Erg. The basin is partially flooded in winter, while in summer pools of water are few and far between. The salt desert and hot air create mirages. Wormwood, fleabane, and retama are the plants that can survive on the shores of the lake.

Inside the basin there are only a few birds: European flamingos, kentish plovers, collared pranticoles, cream-colored coursers, Mediterranean pin-tailed sand grouses, black-bellied sand grouses, and herring gulls. Snipe, stilts, and avocets commonly winter there. All feed on mollusks and crustaceans that live in the mud.

ALGERIA

Cheliff (32)

The Cheliff Gorge which covers about .5 sq. mile (0.8 sq. km), is located in the Ouarsenis massif, south of Algiers, and reached via Blida and Medea. The rocks, carved into layers by the stream, are covered with maquis with mastic trees, strawberry trees, broom with carob trees, and Aleppo pines. The fauna is typically represented by Barbary apes, Algerian hedgehog, jewelled lizards, and European tortoises. There are also many birds; Egyptian vultures, griffon vultures, black kites, long-legged buzzards, and the occasional tawny eagle are joined by the smaller bird life such as yellow wagtails, Senegal's shrikes, green cormorants, subalpine warblers, Dartford warblers, nightingales, serins, and cirl buntings.

There are two other interesting areas in Algeria Lake. La Calle near Annaba, toward the Tunisian border, is rich in aquatic bird life and birds of prey.

MOROCCO

Ketama (33)

The Ketama forest is located in the limey massif of Tidhirina along the chain of the Rif north of Fes. It can be reached from Ketama or from the other slope starting from Targuist. It has skiing facilities, and is famous among tourists as a hunters' paradise.

The lush vegetation is organized into cork oaks on the lower levels and cedars on the more elevated slopes. The fauna is a combination of European and African species. Visitors find ocellated green lizards, fire salamanders, Bibron's agama, red deer, wild boar, Barbary apes, and leopards. Here it is possible to see birds of prey such as black-shouldered kites, goshawks, golden eagles, Bonelli's eagles, and booted eagles. There are numerous Corvidae family, such as ravens, jackdaws, jays, green cormorants and (on the coast); the Turdidae, such as robins, Moussier's redstarts, rock thrushes, blue rock thrushes, and nightingales; and tits, including coal tits, great tits, and blue tits. The largest settlement of monk seals in the Mediterranean is found on the coast of Al Hoceima.

GLOSSARY

adaptation change or adjustment by which a species or individual improves its condition in relationship to its environment.

agriculture the science and art of farming; the work of cultivating the soil, producing crops, and raising livestock.

algae primitive organisms which resemble plants but do not have true roots, stems, or leaves.

archipelago a group or chain of many islands.

aviary a large cage or building for keeping many birds.

biology the science that deals with the origin, history, physical characteristics, life processes, etc. of plants and animals.

conservation the controlled use and systematic protection of natural resources, such as forests and waterways.

continent one of the principal land masses of the earth. Africa, Antarctica, Asia, Europe, North America, South America, and Australia are regarded as continents.

crater a bowl-shaped hole or cavity, such as the mouth of a volcano or the pit formed by a fallen meteor.

cyclone a windstorm with a violent, whirling movement.

deciduous forests forests having trees that shed their leaves at a specific season or stage of growth.

deforestation the clearing of forests or trees. This mass removal of forests was once done for agricultural and industrial purposes.

delta a deposit of sand and soil, usually triangular in shape. Deltas are formed at the mouths of some rivers.

drought a prolonged period of dry weather.

ecology the relationship between organisms and their environment.

ecosystem a system made up of a community of animals, plants, and bacteria and its physical and chemical environment.

environment the circumstances or conditions of a plant or animal's surroundings.

equator an imaginary circle around the earth, equally distant at all points from both the North Pole and the South Pole.

erosion natural processes such as weathering, abrasion, and corrosion, by which material is removed from the earth's surface.

evolution a gradual process in which something changes

into a different and usually more complex or better form.

extinction the process of destroying or extinguishing.

genus a classification of plants or animals with common distinguishing characteristics. A genus is the main subdivision of a family and is made up of a small group of closely related species or of a single species.

geography the descriptive science dealing with the surface of the earth, its divisions into continents and countries, and the climate, plants, animals, natural resources, inhabitants, and industries of the various divisions.

geology the science dealing with the physical nature and history of the earth.

glaciers gigantic moving sheets of ice that covered great areas of the earth in an earlier time.

habitat the areas or type of environment in which a person or other organism normally occurs.

hemisphere any of the halves of the earth. The earth is divided by the equator into the Northern and Southern hemispheres and by a meridian into the Eastern and Western hemispheres.

hydrography the study, description, and mapping of oceans, lakes, and rivers, especially with reference to their navigational and commercial uses.

indigenous existing, growing, or produced naturally in a region or country.

insectivore an animal that eats insects.

lagoon a shallow body of water, especially one separated from the sea by sandbars or coral reefs.

larva the early, immature form of any animal that changes structurally when it becomes an adult.

latitude the angular distance, measured in degrees, north or south from the equator.

lava melted rock that flows from a volcano.

megalith a huge stone, especially one used in prehistoric monuments or in the construction work of ancient times.

migrate to move from one region to another with the change in seasons. Many animals have steady migration patterns.

naturalist a person who studies nature, especially by direct observation of animals and plants.

niche the specific space occupied by an organism within its habitat; a small space or hollow.

nocturnal referring to animals that are active at night.

organism any individual animal or plant having diverse organs and parts that function as a whole to maintain life and its activities.

ornithology the branch of zoology dealing with birds.

photosynthesis the process by which chlorophyll-containing cells in green plants convert sunlight into chemical energy.

physiology the branch of biology dealing with the function and processes of living organisms or their parts and organs.

phytoplankton small, floating aquatic plants.

plankton microscopic plant and animal organisms which float or drift in the ocean or in bodies of fresh water.

refuge shelter or protection from danger or difficulty; a place of safety.

steppe a large plain having few trees.

strait a narrow waterway connecting two large bodies of water.

symbiosis the living together of two kinds of organisms, especially where such an association provides benefits or advantages for both. Algae and fungi in symbiosis form lichens.

valley a stretch of low land lying between hills or mountains and usually having a river or stream flowing through it.

vertebrate having a backbone or spinal column.

zoologist a specialist in the study of animals; their life structure, growth, and classification.

zooplankton floating, often microscopic sea animals.

INDEX

Absolute methods, 49
Abyssal zones, 89-90
Adaptation, 21-22
Aegean Circle, 14
Aeolian Circle, 13
African chameleon, 36-37
Albania, area of interest, 116
Aleppo pine, 28
Algeria, area of interest, 122
Amigos de la Malvasia, 100
Amphiura community, 90
Angel water, 29
Anguidae, lizards, 35-36, 37
Antelope, 57
Areas of natural interest,
    Albania, 116
    Algeria, 122
    Egypt, 121
    France, 109
    Greece, 116
    Israel, 120
    Italy, 111
    Morocco, 122
    Portugal, 106
    Spain, 107
    Syria, 118
    Tunisia, 121
    Turkey, 118
    Yugoslavia, 113
Atlas Mountains, 45
Audouin's gull, 74
Avocet, 86

Balkan Peninsula, 21, 37, 46-47
Banding, birds, 55
Barbary ape, 63
Bearded vulture, 41, 66
Bee-eater, 45
Beetles, 33
Bird censuses, 48-51
    absolute methods, 49-52
    point method, 48, 52
    population, 52
Birds, 10, 17, 43-55, 65-71, 73-79
    banding, 55
    census, 48-52
    ecological indicator, 48-49, 50
    field stations, 53-55
    hunting, 47, 70-71
    migration, 45-47, 86
    necrophagous, 66
    research, 53-55
    wintering, 47
Bittern, 86
Black redstart, 55
Black vulture, 83
Black-wheatear, 13
Blackbryony, 23
Blackcap, 43, 47
Blondel, Jacques, 17
Blue Rock Thrush, 79
Bombina bombina, frog species, 82
Bonelli's eagle, 65-66
Bosporus Straits, 10, 47

Broom, 24
Butcher's broom, 28
Buzzard, 47, 81

Cape Bon, 46
Carob tree, 21, 24, 28, 29
Century plant, 22
Cervus elaphus barbarus, deer
    species, 58
Cervus elaphus corsicanus, deer
    species, 58
Cevennes Mountains, 70
Chalcides ocellatus, lizard species, 35
Chameleon, 36-37
Chiton, 91
Cistus, 24
Classification, animal, 35
Climate, 11-13
Climax, equilibrium, 23
Climax forest, 23, 24
Conservationist, 71
Continental shelf, 89, 90-92
Cork oak, 24, 58
Cork tree, 82
Corsica, 17
Cory's shearwater, 75-76
Crane, 83
Creeping honeysuckle, 23
Cro-Magnon, 6-7
Crocuses, 28
Crows, 45
Curlew, 86
Cyclones, 13

Dalmatian pelican, 83
Dardanelles, 10
Dartford warbler, 43
DDT, 77
Doñana Reserve, 81, 82
Drought, 28
Duck, 83, 86, 99
Dunes, 28
Dunes, coastal, 31-33
Dunlin, 86
Dynamic equilibrium, 16-17

Eagles, 65-66
Earthquake, 13
Ecological barometer, 77
Ecological indicator, 48-49, 77
Ecological niche, 17, 97
Ecologist, 49
Ecology, 14-18, 97
Egret, 83, 86
Egypt, area of interest, 121
Egyptian goose, 86
Egyptian vulture, 41, 66
Elaphe genus, snakes, 37
Eleonora's falcon, 78-79
Elk, 57
Emerald lizard, 35, 37
Endangered species, 17
Endemic species, 18-19
Erosion, 13, 28

Euphorbia, bush species, 79
Euphorbia dendroides, shrub species, 31
Euphorbia genus, plants, 71
Euphorbiaceae family, shrubs, 31
European black vulture, 66
European swamp turtle, 41
Eurynebria complanata, beetle species, 33
Evergreen oak tree, 23
Extinction, 16-17, 19, 65, 67-71

Fallow deer, 57-58
Family, 35
Fan palm, 31
Field stations, bird, 53-55
Finches, 45, 47
Flamingo, 86
France, area of interest, 109

Garden warbler, 43
Gargano peninsula, 16
Garigue, 28, 30, 31, 43
Gecko, 36
Gekkonidae, lizard family, 36
Genetic drift, 19
Genus, 35
Gibralter, 47
Glaciers, 9, 21
Goat, wild, 59-61
Godwit, 86
Golden eagle, 41
Grasses, 32-33
Greece, area of interest, 116
Green cormorant, 75
Greenbriar, 23
Griffon vulture, 66-67, 70, 71
Gull, 86

Hardun, 36
Herodotus, 14
Herodotus zone, 89
Heron, 83, 86
Herring gull, 73
Holly oak, 29
Holm oak, 23-24, 28, 58, 61
Homer, 98
Homo erectus, 6
Homo sapiens, 6
Humid zones, 48
Hunting, birds, 47, 70-71
Hydrography, 9
Hyla araborea, frog species, 82

Iberian Peninsula, 45
Ice Age, 21
Immigration, 16
Imperial eagle, 65, 82, 83
Insecticide, 77
Insects, 33
Introduction, 21-22
Irises, 28
Israel, area of interest, 120
Italy, area of interest, 111

Jewelled lizard, 35
Judas tree, 21
Juniper tree, 28

Kermes oak, 24
Kingfisher, 81
Kite, 47
Krakatoa, volcano, 14

Lacertidae, lizard family, 35
Ladder snake, 37
Lataste's viper, 81
Laurel tree, 29
Lavender, 28
Leopard snake, 37
Lime tree, 22
Linear itinerary, 52
Lipari, volcano, 13
Lizards, 35-37

Macoma community, 91
Mammals, 57-63
   fallow deer, 57-58
   mouflon, 58-59
   ungulates, 57-61
   wild goat, 59-61
Mapping, bird census, 49
Maquis, 28-31, 41, 43-55, 83
Marmora's warbler, 43
Marshes, 81-87
   environments, 81-82
   seasons, 83-86
Mastic shrub, 21, 28
Mastic tree, 29-30
Mauremys caspica, turtle species, 41
Melanin, 37
Migration, 45-47
Monk Seal, 97
Moray eel, 37
Morocco, area of interest, 122
Mouflon, 58-59
Mount Parnassus, 21
Mountain Chain, Mediterranean, 9
Mt. Etna, volcano, 14
Myrtle, 21, 24, 28, 29

Natrix genus, snakes, 37
Nature Conservation, 17-19
Neanderthal, 6
Newton, Jan, 77
Niethammer, Gunther, 61

Oleander, 21, 30
Olive tree, 24, 28
Overgrazing, 28

Pantelleria, volcano, 14
Patella, 91, 93
Pelagian Islands, 46
Pelagic fish, 95
Pelicaniformes, pelican order, 75
Perching birds, 83
Peregrine falcon, 77
Phlegraean Fields, 14
Phrygana, 28

Pine tree, 23
Pinniped, 98
Plane tree, 21
Plant association, 22-28
Plant succession, 22-23
Plover, 86
Point method, bird census, 48, 52
Population, birds, 52
Population density, birds, 52
Porcupine, 61-62
Porcupine, crested, 61
Portugal, area of interest, 106
Pozzuoli, volcano, 14
Pratincoles, 86
Prickly pear, 22
Primate, 63
Procida Island, 53
Pseudopus apodus, lizard species, 36
Purple Gallinule, 100-101

Rabbit, wild, 62
Rana psulenta, frog species, 82
Rana ridibiundfa, frog species, 86
Rat snake, 37
Red deer, 57, 58
Red-water tree, 61
Redshank, 86
Reindeer, 57
Reptiles, 35-41
Researchers, bird, 53-55
Rhizome, 32
Rif Mountains, 45
Ringed snake, 82
Rockroses, 28
Rodents, 61-63
Roller, 45
Rosemary, 28
Ruff, 86
Ruppell's warbler, 43

Sage, 28
Santorini, volcano, 14
Sardinia, 17
Sardinian warbler, 43
Scincidae, lizard family, 35
Sea of Thetys, 9
Sea turtle, 101-103
Sedimentation, 81
Selvagens Islands, 75
Shags, 75
Shorebirds, 81
Short-toed eagle, 37-40, 81
Shrikes, 83
Sicily, 17
Silt, 81
Skink, 35
Skylarks, 44-45
Small-spotted genet, 82
Snakes, 37-41
Soil, 13
Spain, area of interest, 107
Species, 35
Spoonbill, 86
Spurge, 28, 31
Starlings, 47

Steppe, 28, 31
Stilt, 86
Stock-rearing, 66
Stork, 47
Strait of Gibraltar, 10-11, 45
Strait of Messina, 47
Straits, 10-11
Strawberry tree, 23, 24, 28, 29, 30
Stromboli, volcano, 13
Sturgeon, 95
Suez Canal, 10, 12
Swallow, 86
Sylvia genus, birds, 43
Sylviids, 43-44
Symbiosis, 36

Tellina community, 91
Terns, 86
Terra Amata, Italy, 6
Testudo genus, tortoise, 40
Thrushes, 47
Thyme, 28

Tinbergen, Nikolaas, 73
Tomillares, 28
Tortoise, 40-41, 81
    disappearance, 41
    travel ability, 41
Tree frog, 82
Tree heath, 24, 28, 30
Tunisia, area of interest, 121
Turkey, area of interest, 118
Turnstone, 86
Turtle, 40-41, 101-103
    disappearance, 41
    food, 41
    reproduction, 102-103

Ungulates, 57-61

Vegetation, 13, 21-33
    drought, 28
    dunes, 31-32
    and sunlight, 23
    varieties, 21-22

Venus community, 90
Viburnum, 23
Vivara Island, 53, 55
Volcano, 13-14
Vulcano, volcano, 13
Vulture, 66-71, 86

Warbler, 43
Wetlands, 81, 86
Wheatgrass, 32
White throat, 13
White wagtails, 86
White-headed duck, 99-100
White-tailed eagle, 83, 86
White-throat, 43
Willow warblers, 47
Winds, 13
Wintering, 47-48
Wood pigeon, 81
Woodpeckers, 83

Yugoslavia, area of interest, 113

DATE DUE

	DATE DUE